S0-BOH-912

EVERYTHING'S A PUZZLE

Copyright 1953, Unicorn Books, Inc.

PRINTED IN THE UNITED STATES OF AMERICA

+ BIRTHPLACE OF ROMEO AND JULIET + YPS

− Nickname For Alfred, *In 2 Letters* + Opposite Of THICK

+ − − NLA

E	V	E	R	Y	T	H	I	N	G	'S

A

+ + ZZ −

+ − Synonym For Anger Or Fury − T

P	U	Z	Z	L	E

UNICORN BOOKS, INC.

Table
of
Contents

	Page
Rebus Puzzles	1-130
Picture Puzzle	131
Whose Portraits Are on Your Money?	132
Highest and Lowest Points in the World	133
How Deep Is the Ocean?	134
Author! Author!	135
Distances	136
World's Great Inventions Quiz	137-139
Art Treasures	140
Nobel Prizes Won by Americans	141
How Much Above Par Are You?	142
Wise Men's Sayings	143-149
Famous People Quiz	150-161
Correct Solutions to Rebus Puzzles	162-178
Answers to Famous People Quiz	179
Answers to Quiz on Page 135	180
Answers to World's Great Inventions	181-182
Correct Solutions to Wise Men's Sayings	183-184

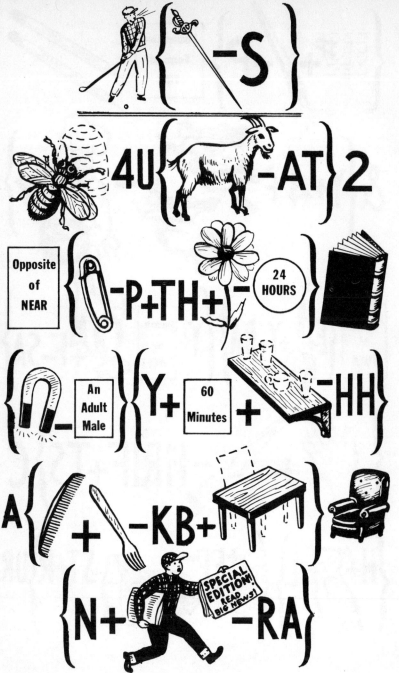

(A)

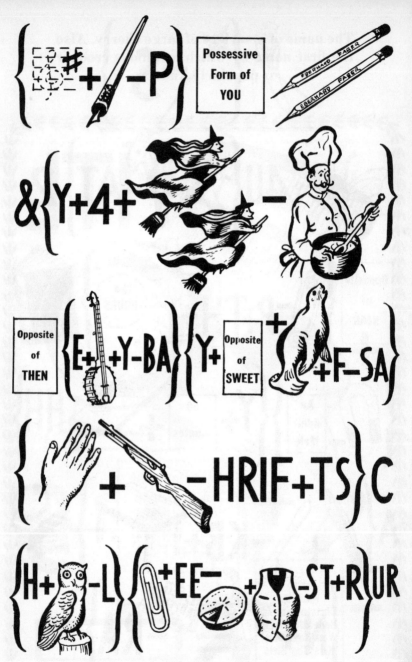

(Solution to pages (A) and (B) on page 184)

(B)

The name of a variety of large cherry. Also the first name by which a famous crooner is popularly known.

+ ITL

+

−

+ Last Name Of An American Confederate Army General Whose First Two Initials Were R. E.

−S

− A 9-Letter Plant Much Hung At Christmastime, Beneath Which You Boys May Kiss The Girls

=

Solution is the last name of a beloved American comedian outstanding for his nose as well as his humor.

+IDO+

First Month Of The Year

+N+

Last Name Of First Chief Justice Of The United States Supreme Court

−AS+E

=

If you have it, you've got plenty of energy and vim.

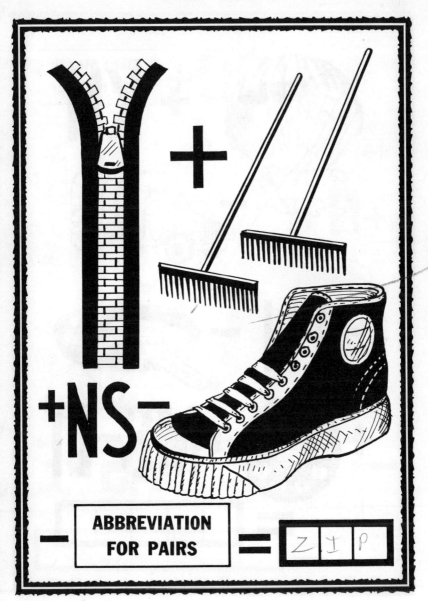

The last name of two Americans, both of
whom were Presidents of the United States.

In the summer, one of nature's most pleas-
ant creations.

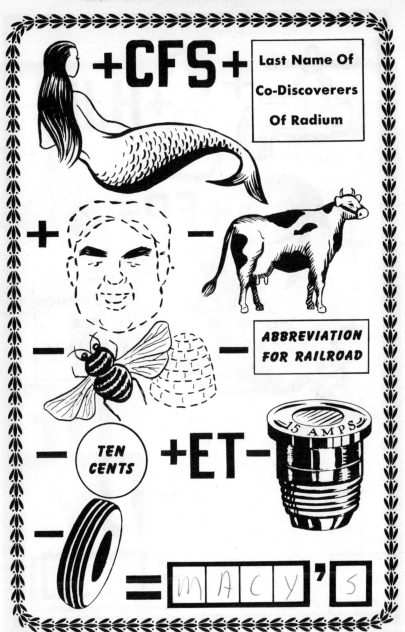

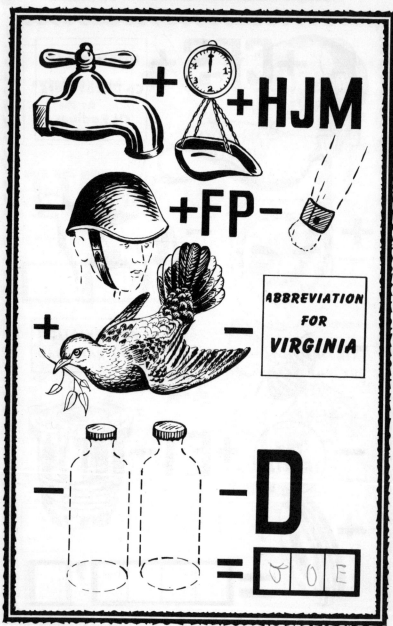

Solution is the name of the most important yearly baseball event in the United States.

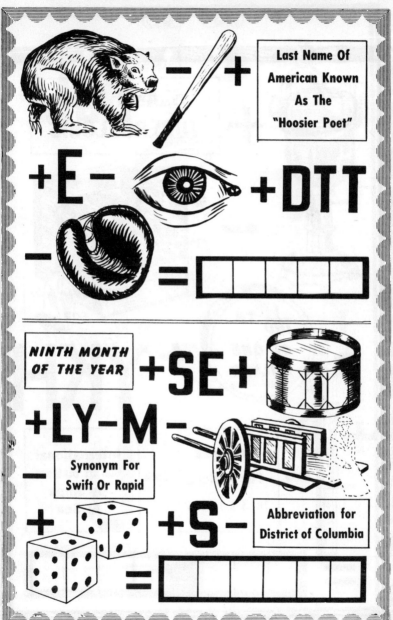

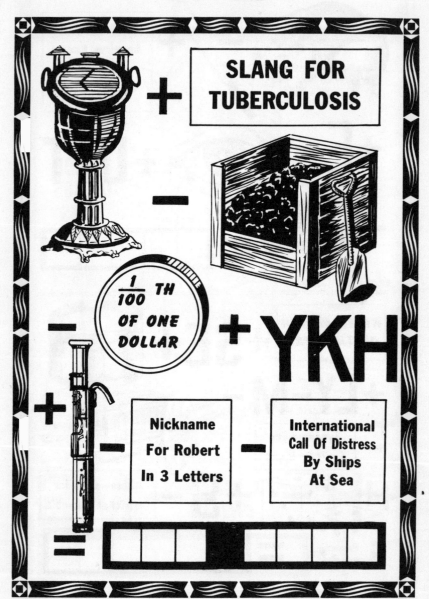

Solution is the first name of an American actress whose father and grandfather held important political office in our land.

First name of an American girl who was
a wonderful shot with a gun.

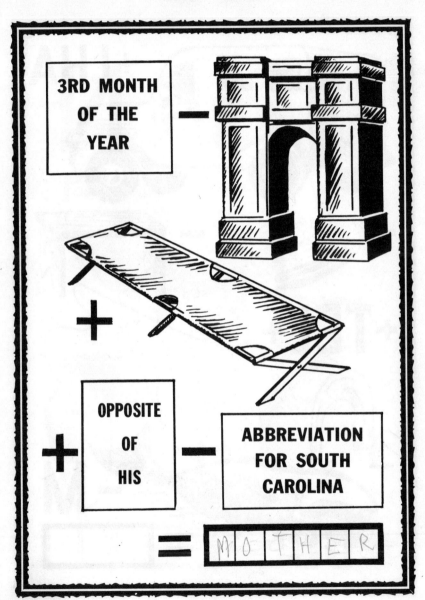

This can mean either a gratuity, or a useful
hint, or the extremity of a thing.

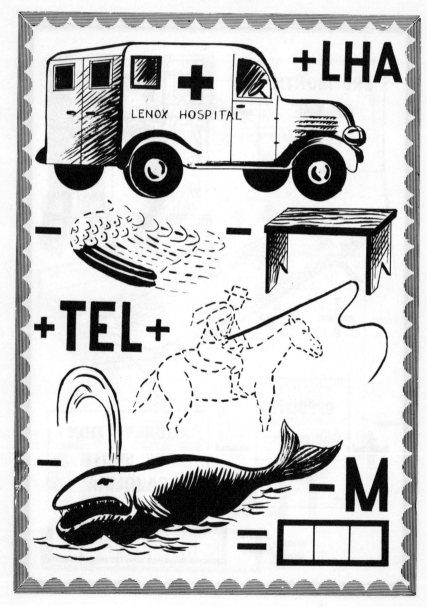

The last name of a British naval hero who fell in love with Lady Hamilton.

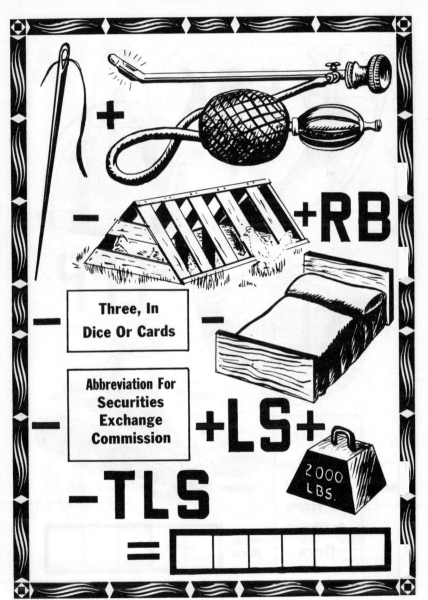

3-Letter Verb Meaning To Have A Short Doze

= SLEEP

The first name by which the female portion of an American husband-wife radio team is popularly known.

The last name of an American political
leader who was the youngest governor in
the history of Minnesota.

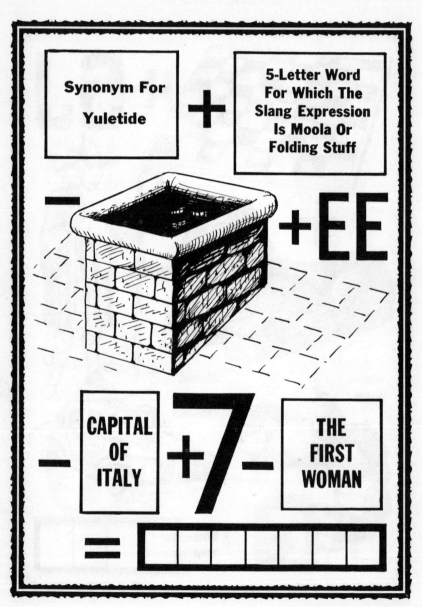

Synonym For Yuletide + 5-Letter Word For Which The Slang Expression Is Moola Or Folding Stuff

− +EE

− CAPITAL OF ITALY +7− THE FIRST WOMAN

= ☐☐☐☐☐☐☐

A verb meaning to clasp tightly in one's arms.

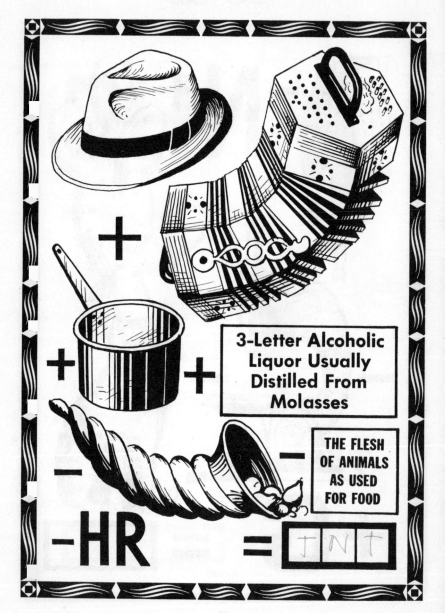

This is supposed to begin at home.

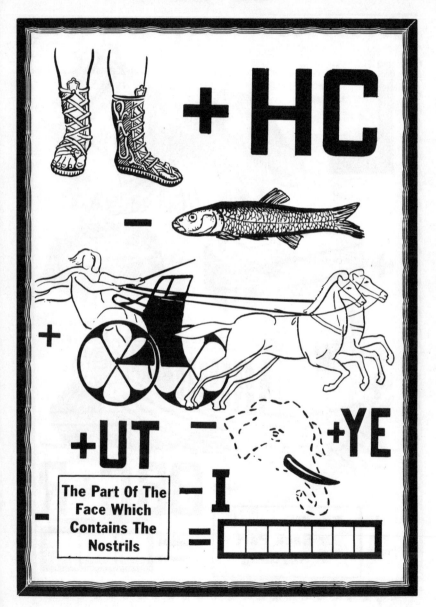

The Part Of The Face Which Contains The Nostrils

21

The Hindmost Or Back Part Of Anything

The abbreviated name of a baseball team, very often successful in picking off the big-time pennants.

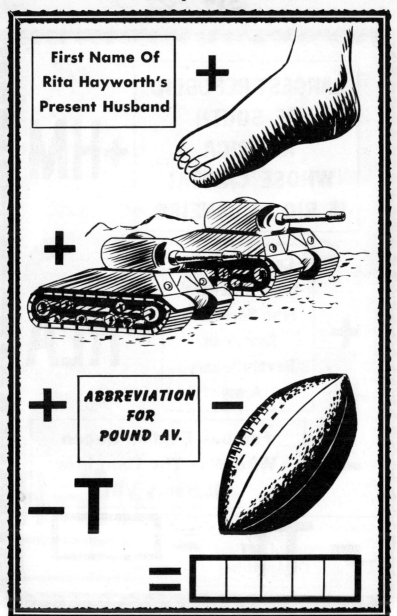

First Name Of Rita Hayworth's Present Husband

+

+

+ ABBREVIATION FOR POUND AV. −

−T

=

The name of a girl, and also of one of the twelve months.

≈≈≈   ≈≈≈

LARGEST REPUBLIC OF SOUTH AMERICA WHOSE CAPITAL IS RIO DE JANEIRO +HM

+ **Last Name Of French General Who Served In American Revolutionary Army** −RLA

− **Famous English Queen Who Was The Daughter Of Henry VIII**

− TF = MAY

The last name of an American army general of World War II, famous for slapping a soldier, as well as for his competence.

In the direction which is to the right of a
person facing the setting sun or west.

4-Letter
Noun For A
Large Branch
Of A Tree

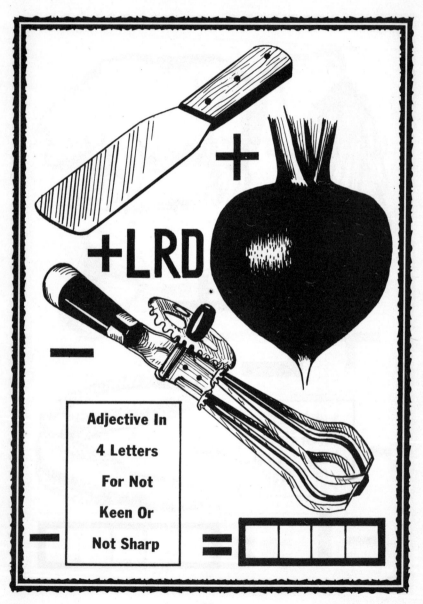

Romeo and Juliet, and Antony and Cleopatra, are some outstanding examples of them.

3-Letter Slang Word For A Roll, As Of Paper Money

First 3 Letters Of A European Republic, Whose Former Capital Was Berlin

= LOVERS

The name of a Chinese breed of dog. Also
U. S. army slang for food.

9-Letter Word For The Queen Of Wines, Effervescent And Usually White

+

−

3-Letter Abbreviated Form Of SAMUEL

−

− AGN = M E S S

A man of good breeding or polite manners.

The name of the greatest book of them all.

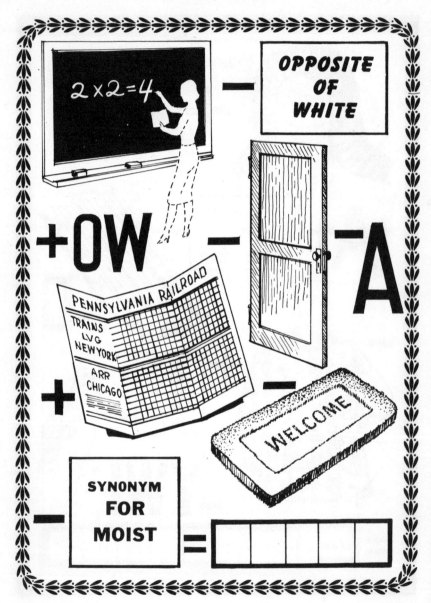

The last name of a famous Dutch painter who died in poverty, although his masterpieces are today worth fortunes.

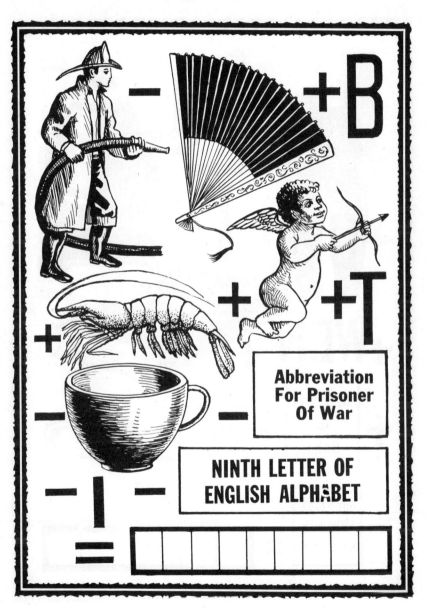

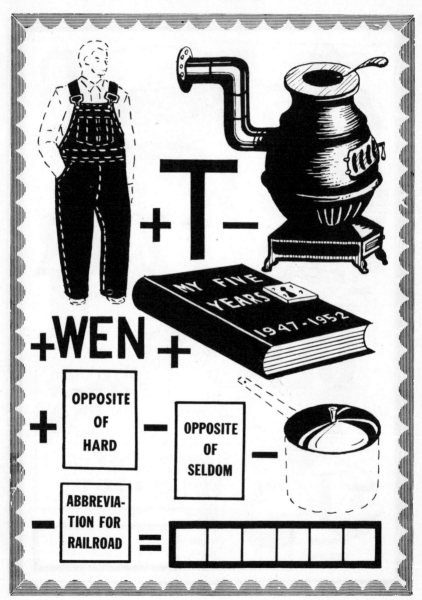

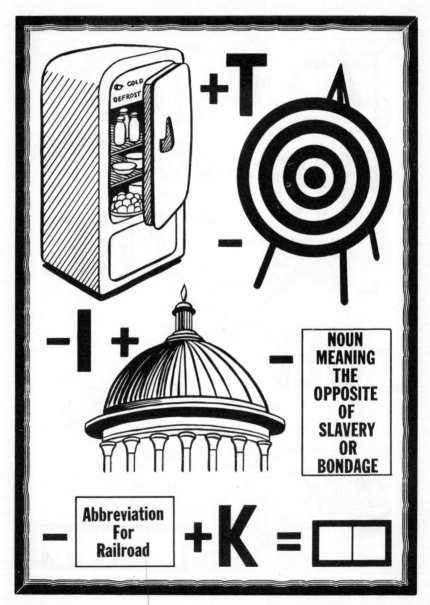

Solution is the assumed last name of a Russian Bolshevik leader, former head of the Soviet government.

ABBREVIATION FOR NORTH CAROLINA

The name of a city in Ohio, and the last name of an Italian navigator who made an important discovery.

The last name of an American army general who was elected President of the United States.

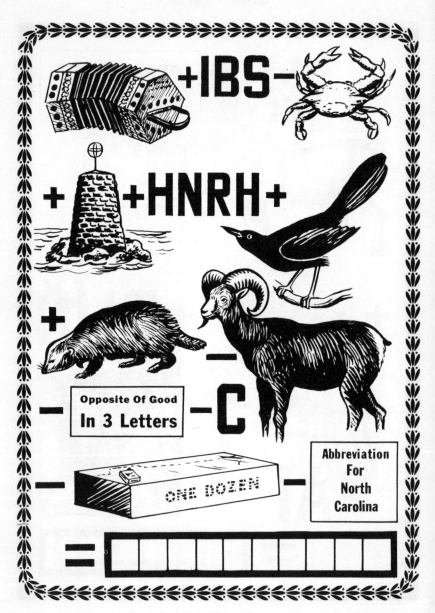

You find her in a palace, and also in a deck
of cards.

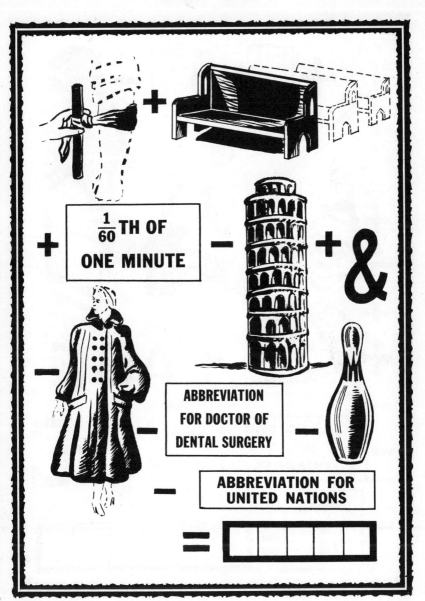

A verb meaning to be agreeable or to give pleasure or satisfaction.

Solution is the last name of an American comedian famous for his "banjo" eyes and his song about Susie.

4-LETTER NOUN FOR AN ELEVATION SMALLER THAN A MOUNTAIN

+LTP-

ABBREVIATION FOR KITCHEN POLICE

-F =

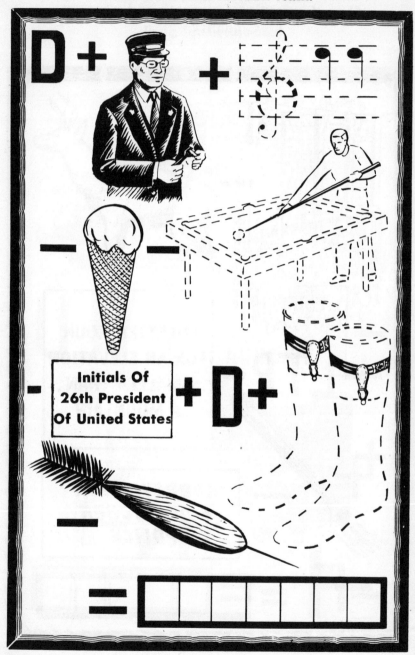

Solution is the name of a man-made miracle fiber of exceptional strength and wearing quality.

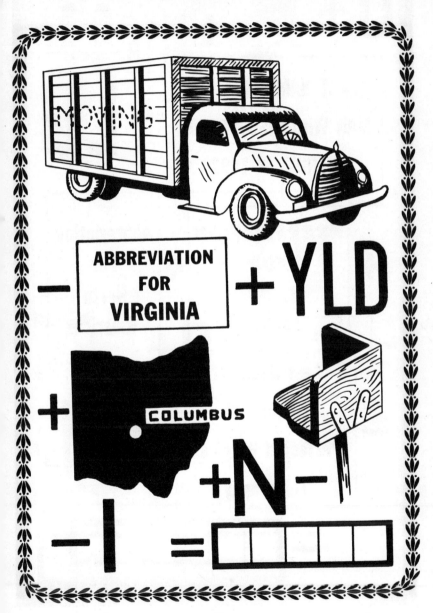

The name of a measure. It's 4 pecks.

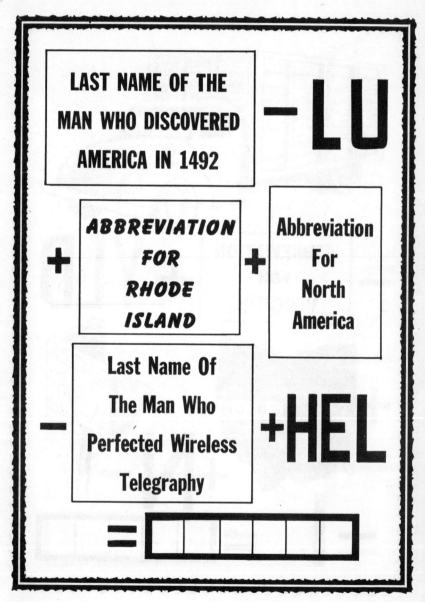

LAST NAME OF THE MAN WHO DISCOVERED AMERICA IN 1492 − LU

+ ABBREVIATION FOR RHODE ISLAND

+ Abbreviation For North America

− Last Name Of The Man Who Perfected Wireless Telegraphy

+HEL

= ☐☐☐☐☐☐

A unit of organization in an army, being next below a brigade and usually commanded by a colonel.

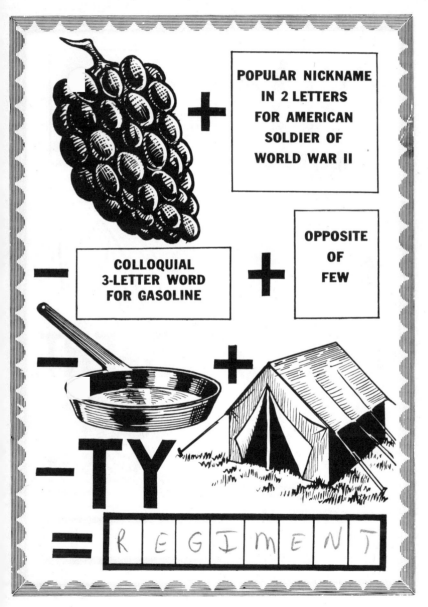

POPULAR NICKNAME IN 2 LETTERS FOR AMERICAN SOLDIER OF WORLD WAR II

COLLOQUIAL 3-LETTER WORD FOR GASOLINE

OPPOSITE OF FEW

-TY

= R E G I M E N T

Solution is the last name of the Republican who was elected in 1952 to be next Vice-President of the United States.

'Tis said this is what makes the mare go.
Others call it the root of all evil. Anyway,
you can't pay the rent without it.

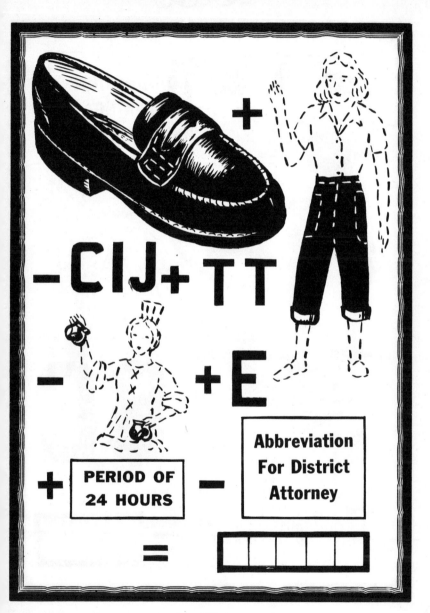

−CIJ+ TT

− +E

+ PERIOD OF 24 HOURS − Abbreviation For District Attorney

=

A short form of Thomas, and the first name
of one of Mark Twain's young heroes.

+T−

+

−BC

3-LETTER
VERB
MEANING
TO BE
MISTAKEN
OR TO STRAY

−

= TOM

The name of an odoriferous cheese.

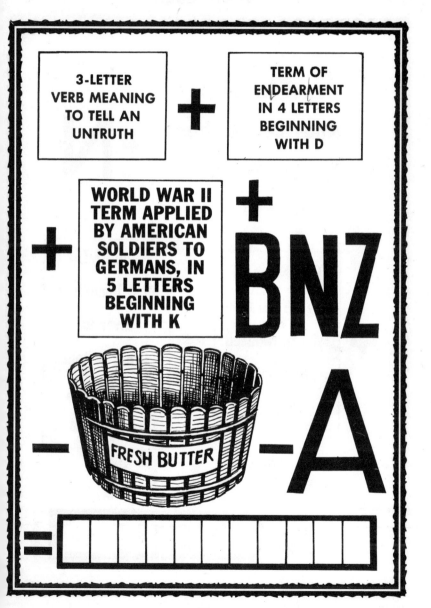

3-LETTER VERB MEANING TO TELL AN UNTRUTH

+

TERM OF ENDEARMENT IN 4 LETTERS BEGINNING WITH D

+

WORLD WAR II TERM APPLIED BY AMERICAN SOLDIERS TO GERMANS, IN 5 LETTERS BEGINNING WITH K

+

BNZ

− FRESH BUTTER **− A**

= ☐☐☐☐☐☐☐☐☐☐☐☐☐

The nickname of the Englishman who was British Prime Minister during World War II.

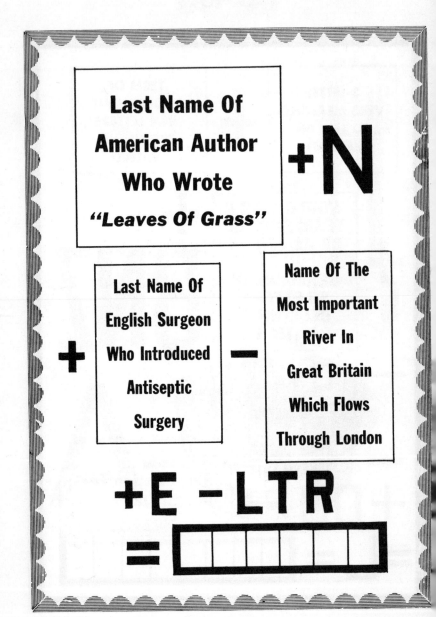

Solution is the noun for any of various alcoholic mixed drinks.

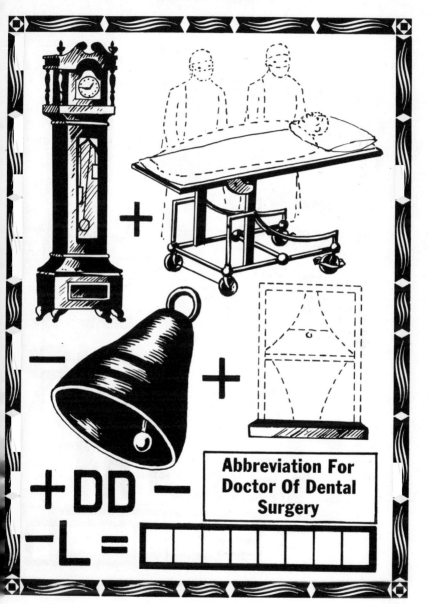

Solution is the name of a place in England where a famous horse race is held annually on the Downs.

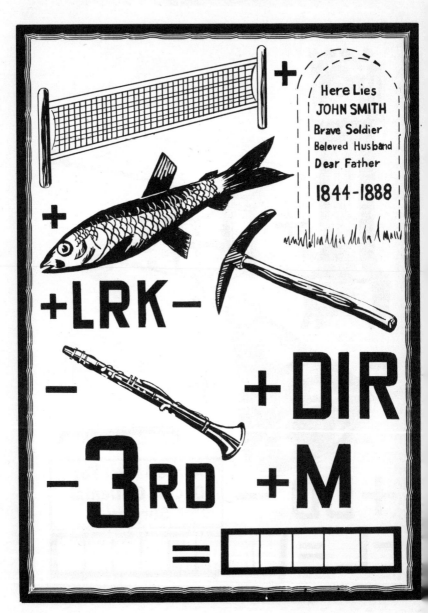

Solution is the noun meaning tripping the light fantastic.

A NATIVE OF DENMARK +

+OSG−

−E−

Current Term To Denote Guerrilla Fighters In Modern Philippines

=

The last name of a popular cowboy star.

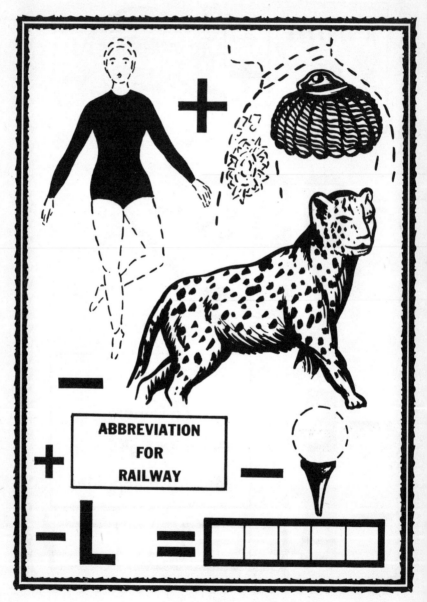

There's no place in the world like it.

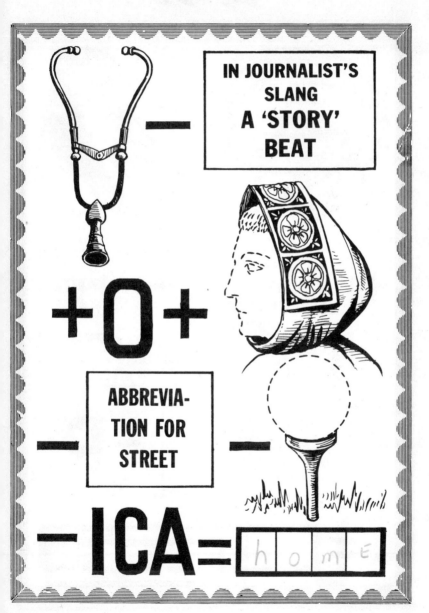

IN JOURNALIST'S SLANG A 'STORY' BEAT

+O+

ABBREVIATION FOR STREET

−ICA= h o m E

The name of a girl, and of a famous city in Italy.

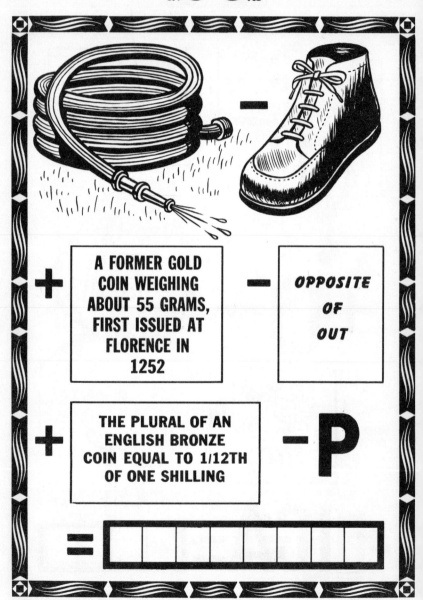

A FORMER GOLD COIN WEIGHING ABOUT 55 GRAMS, FIRST ISSUED AT FLORENCE IN 1252

OPPOSITE OF OUT

THE PLURAL OF AN ENGLISH BRONZE COIN EQUAL TO 1/12TH OF ONE SHILLING

- P

=

The keeper or operator of a mill (but not a
gin-mill).

Last Name Of
American Author
Who Wrote
"The Raven"
+
Last Name
Of English
Poet Who Wrote
"Paradise Lost"

+11+
**ABBREVIATION
FOR UNION OF
SOCIALIST SOVIET
REPUBLICS**

**Last Name Of
English Author
Of *"Treasure
Island"***
−
*OPPOSITE
OF
DOWN*

−OE = ▯▯▯▯▯▯▯

The last name of a former chief justice of the U. S. Supreme Court.

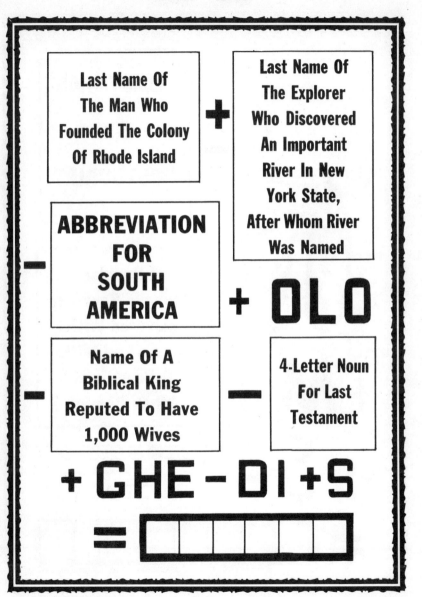

Last Name Of The Man Who Founded The Colony Of Rhode Island

+

Last Name Of The Explorer Who Discovered An Important River In New York State, After Whom River Was Named

− ABBREVIATION FOR SOUTH AMERICA

+ OLO

− Name Of A Biblical King Reputed To Have 1,000 Wives

− 4-Letter Noun For Last Testament

+ GHE − DI + S

= ⬜⬜⬜⬜⬜⬜⬜

The last name of a former American Communist who put the finger on a U. S. Government official.

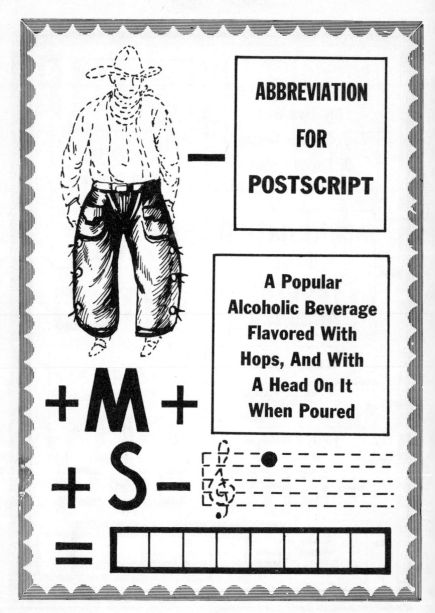

ABBREVIATION FOR POSTSCRIPT

A Popular Alcoholic Beverage Flavored With Hops, And With A Head On It When Poured

Recently coined word for a combination breakfast and lunch, popular on Sundays.

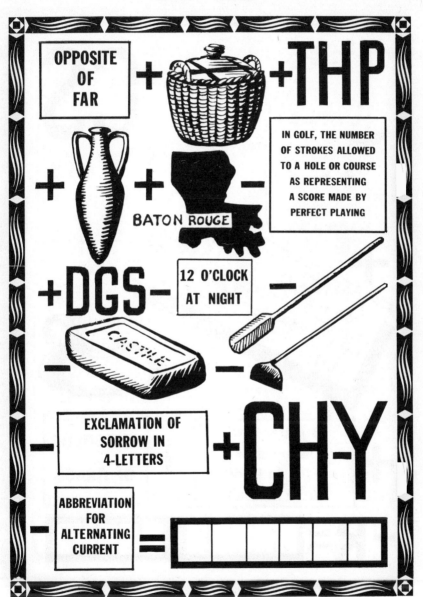

OPPOSITE OF FAR + [basket] +THP

+ [vase] + [Baton Rouge, Louisiana] − [IN GOLF, THE NUMBER OF STROKES ALLOWED TO A HOLE OR COURSE AS REPRESENTING A SCORE MADE BY PERFECT PLAYING]

+DGS− 12 O'CLOCK AT NIGHT −

− CASTILE − [brush] −

− EXCLAMATION OF SORROW IN 4-LETTERS +CH-Y

− ABBREVIATION FOR ALTERNATING CURRENT = [ ][ ][ ][ ][ ][ ]

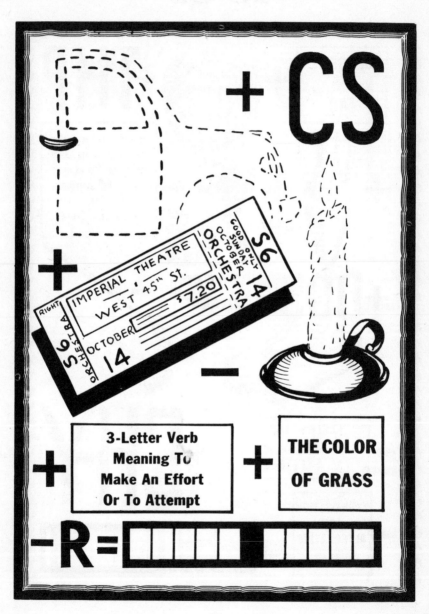

A four-legged animal that some say is man's best friend.

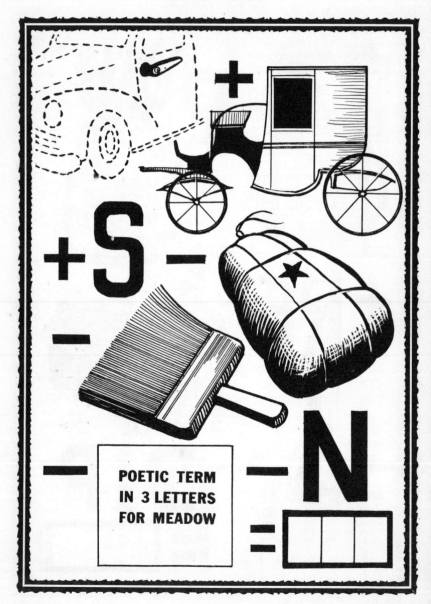

POETIC TERM
IN 3 LETTERS
FOR MEADOW

The last name of an American naval officer
who died of yellow fever.

6-LETTER NOUN MEANING UNSIGHTLY SWELLING ON THE FOOT ESPECIALLY THE BIG TOE

= R E R R Y

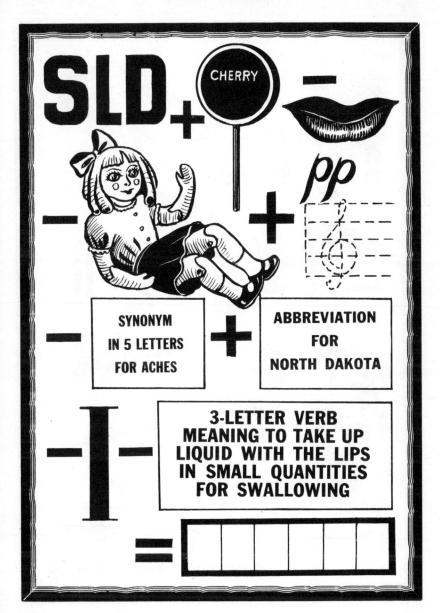

You get them at the grocer's.

A word used to express dissent, denial, or refusal.

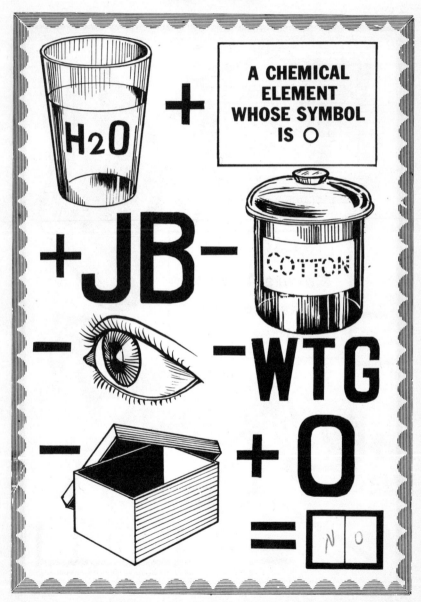

A yellow solid, derived from milk, good to eat when spread on bread.

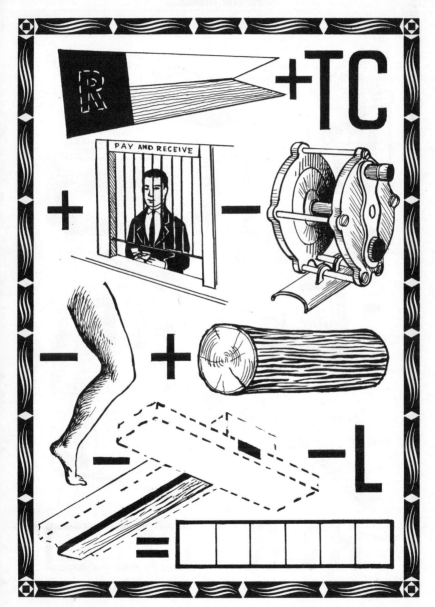

A disease characterized by painful inflammation of the joints, chiefly those in the feet and hands, and by excess of uric acid in the blood.

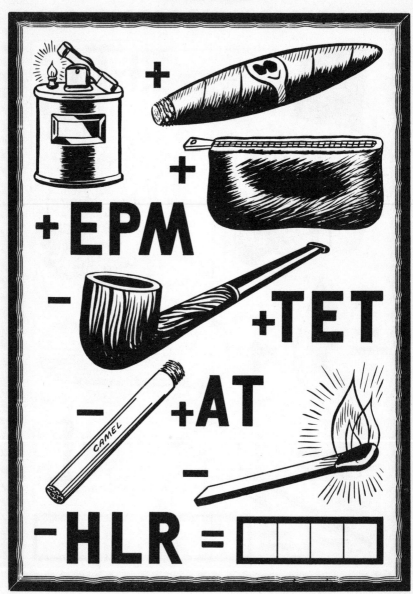

The name of the N.E. peninsula of the North American continent, separating Hudson Bay from the Atlantic Ocean.

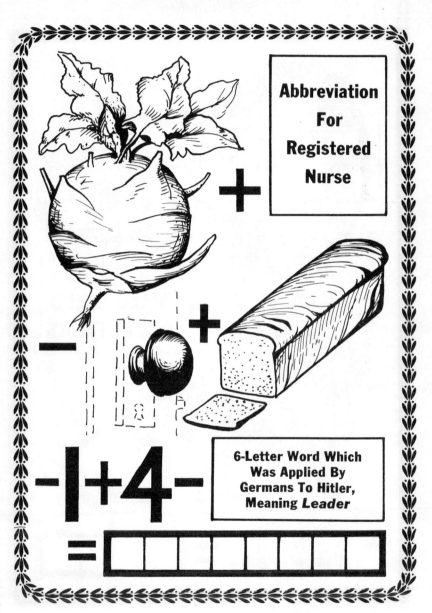

Abbreviation For Registered Nurse

+

−

+

-1+4-

6-Letter Word Which Was Applied By Germans To Hitler, Meaning *Leader*

=

The name of a university and of a lock.

Famous Italian Renaissance
Painter, Sculptor, Architect
And Poet, Who Decorated The
Sistine Chapel With Paintings That
Are World Masterpieces

+ BIY -

LAST NAME OF
INVENTOR OF
THE TELEPHONE

-

STATE OF WHICH
LANSING IS
THE CAPITAL

+ALE

- EO = ▢▢▢▢▢

Your Mother and your Father, and you'll
never get better ones.

Last Name Of English Writer,
The Greatest Of Dramatic
Poets, Known As The
"Bard Of Avon"

+W−

Last Name Of
Irish Author Who
Wrote *"Candida"*

−

4-Letter Verb
Meaning To
Search For
Or Look For

+NTS

=

Solution is the name of a material, also the last name of an American politician imprisoned for robbing New York City.

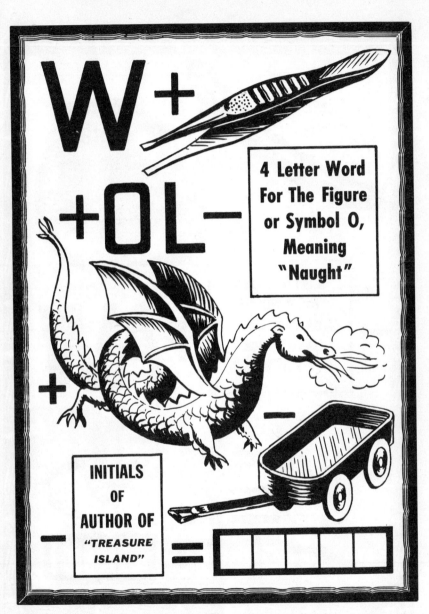

The skin of certain animals with a fine, soft, thick hairy coating. Makes nice coats. The ladies love it.

+

4-LETTER WORD FOR A FUR OF A NATURAL BROWN COLOR, MUCH PRIZED BY WOMEN

− +AW

− H_2O −

−TF= ☐☐☐

A two-legged fowl, good when fried, broiled,
boiled, roasted, or in a salad.

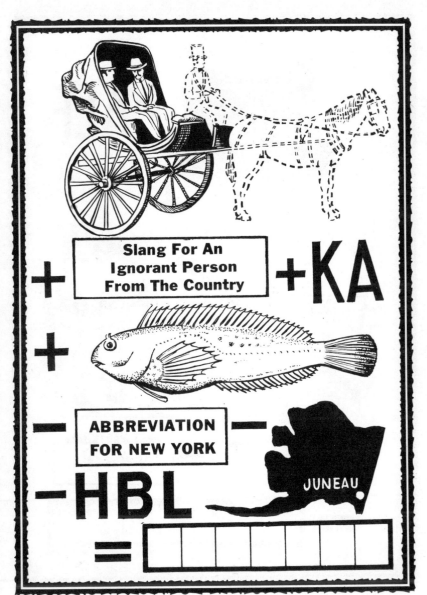

The name of a long, narrow boat with a high peak at each end, used on the canals of Venice.

Last name of four popular American male singers.

Solution is a word meaning two in cards or dice.

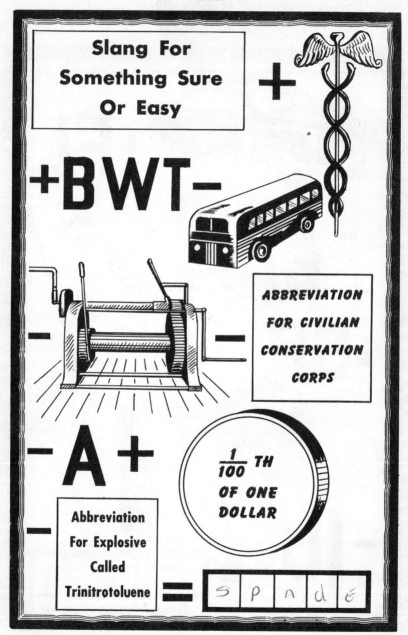

Slang For Something Sure Or Easy +

+BWT-

- -

ABBREVIATION FOR CIVILIAN CONSERVATION CORPS

-A+

$\frac{1}{100}$ TH OF ONE DOLLAR

- Abbreviation For Explosive Called Trinitrotoluene = S p a d e

An adverb meaning after the usual or proper time, or after delay.

The last name of a well-known American newspaper columnist who died in the Pacific during World War II.

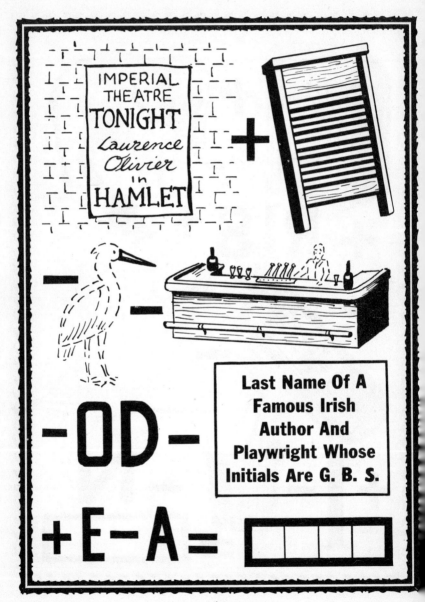

IMPERIAL THEATRE TONIGHT Laurence Olivier in HAMLET + washboard

− bird − bar

−OD−

Last Name Of A Famous Irish Author And Playwright Whose Initials Are G. B. S.

+E−A= ☐☐☐☐

Initials of the 33rd President of the United States.

An organized body of men trained and
equipped for war.

-RW
+

-ER +

OPPOSITE
OF COLD

5-Letter
Verb
Meaning
To Strike
or Beat
Heavily
with A
Dull Sound

−
+HMY−

=

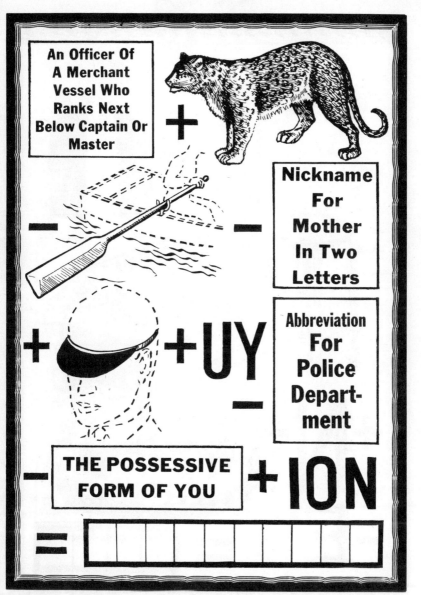

An Officer Of A Merchant Vessel Who Ranks Next Below Captain Or Master

+

−

−

Nickname For Mother In Two Letters

+

+UY

Abbreviation For Police Department

−

−

THE POSSESSIVE FORM OF YOU

+ION

=

The last name of a famous German musical composer whose instrument par excellence was the organ.

Solution is the last name of the defeated 1952 Democratic candidate for Vice-President of the United States.

The name of a city of Florida, famous as a
U. S. center for the manufacture of Havana
clear cigars.

**LAST QUEEN OF
EGYPT AND
FAMOUS SIREN**

+N

–

**Roman Emperor
Who Fiddled While
Rome Burned**

–CLP+

**ABBREVIATION
FOR
MOUNTED
POLICE**

–A+A

= ▢▢▢▢▢

Name of an institution of learning of the highest grade, having various schools and faculties.

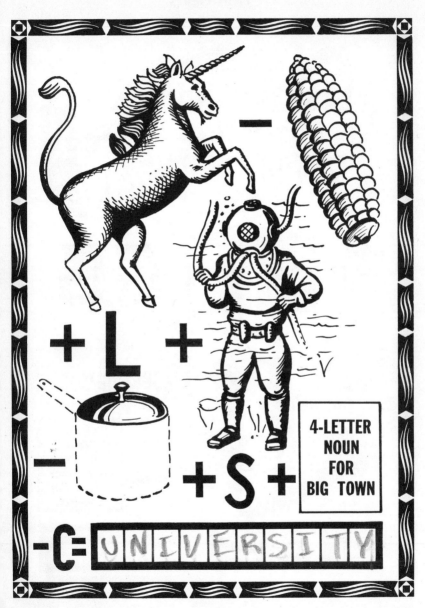

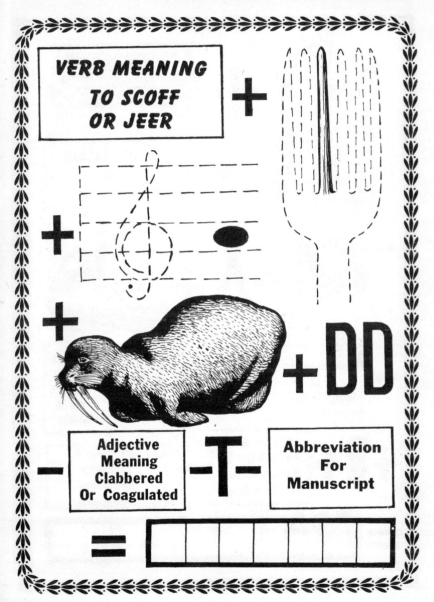

Solution is the word for the president or
head of a yacht-club or boat-club.

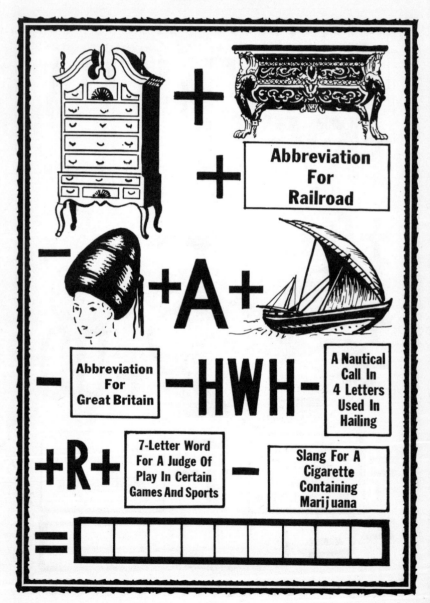

98

An adjective meaning either the opposite
of soft, or the opposite of easy.

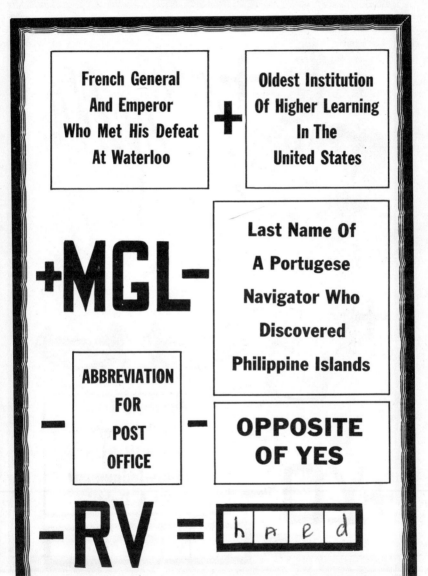

The name of a European country defeated in World War II.

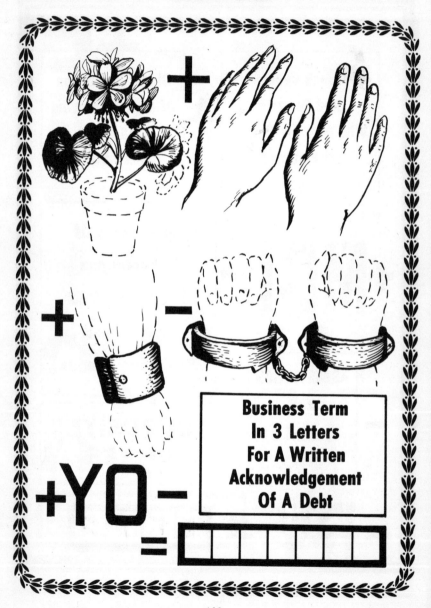

**Business Term
In 3 Letters
For A Written
Acknowledgement
Of A Debt**

A verb meaning to trade by exchange of commodities, rather than by the use of money.

The name of a substance said to be the clearest solid known.

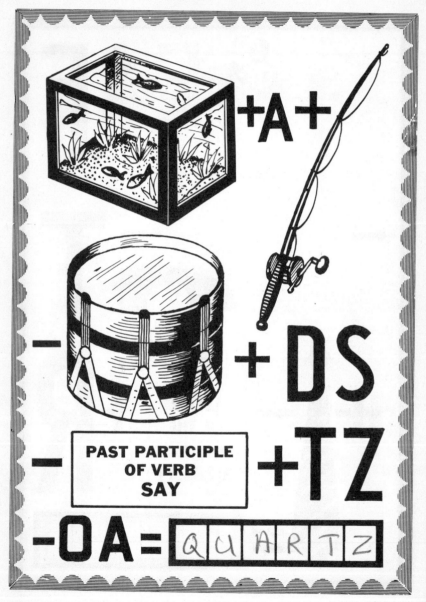

+A+

− ... **+DS**

− PAST PARTICIPLE OF VERB SAY **+TZ**

−OA = Q U A R T Z

104

An adjective meaning the opposite of
complicated.

105

Name of a mountain range of E. Russia, often considered the boundary between Europe and Asia.

DISTANCE OF 3 FEET

+

-E

- +AL

= URAL

An adjective meaning lukewarm.

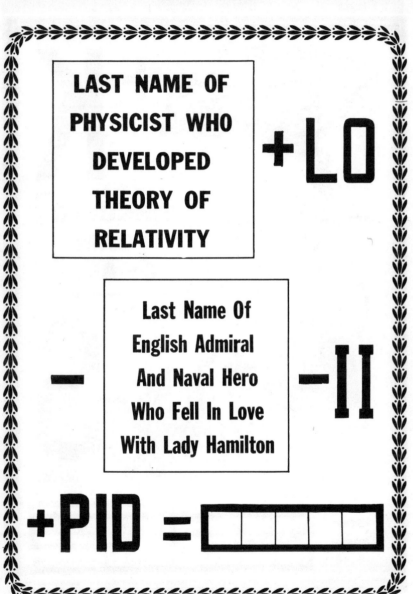

The last name of a Norwegian traitor.

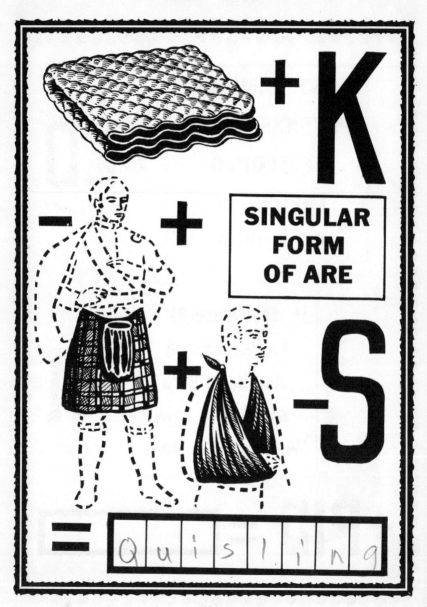

The name of a city of Poland.

The name of a cooked meat that goes fine
with Yorkshire pudding.

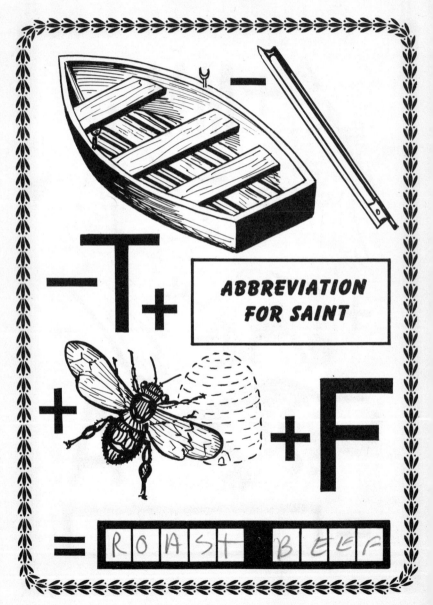

= R O A S T   B E E F

Solution is the last name of a convicted
American gambler.

Last Name of Man Who Discovered America In 1492 +**LR**

−

Alcoholic Liquor Distilled From Molasses And Popular In Cuba + WELCOME

− *ABBREVIATION FOR ANTE MERIDIEM*

+ **Exclamation To Express Greeting Used Over Telephone** −**H**

= C O S T E L L O

Abbreviation for a body of the representatives of many nations, formerly presided over by Trygvie Lie.

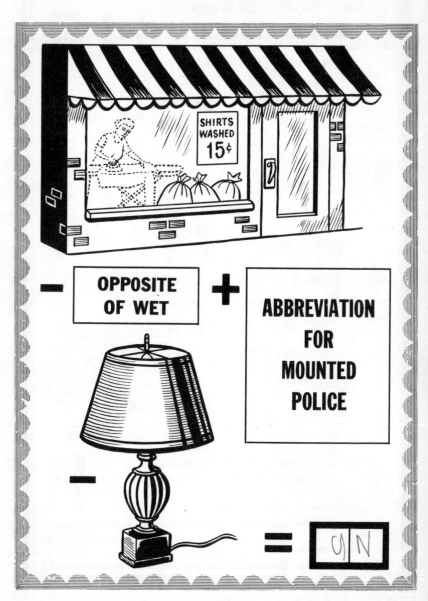

SHIRTS WASHED 15¢

− OPPOSITE OF WET + ABBREVIATION FOR MOUNTED POLICE

− = UN

114

Forms of an element having the same atomic number but different atomic weights.

= I S O T O P E S

115

The name of the chief magistrate of the old republics of Venice and Genoa.

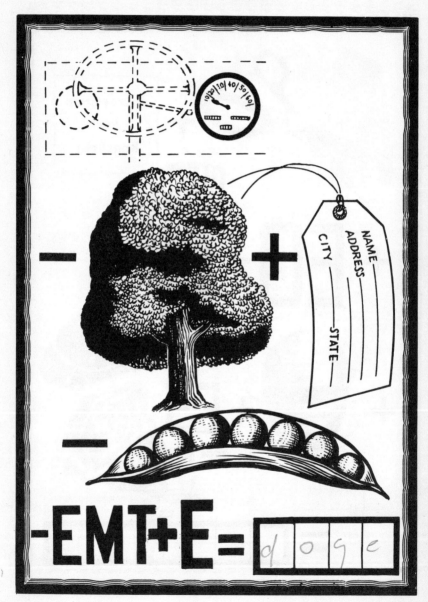

-EMT+E = d o g e

The name of a city in Turkey.

Abbreviation For Daughters Of American Revolution

+A

2-Letter Short Form For Edward

= A N K A R A

The name of a country of Asia which is the scene of present-day fighting.

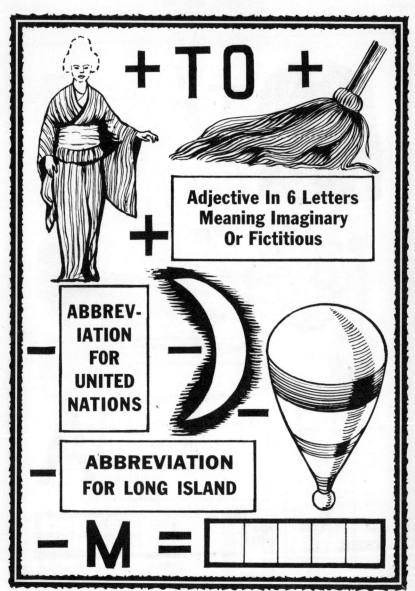

+ TO +

Adjective In 6 Letters Meaning Imaginary Or Fictitious

+

ABBREVIATION FOR UNITED NATIONS

-

ABBREVIATION FOR LONG ISLAND

- M =

What's left of an ear of corn when you fin-
ish eating the corn.

One of the two sons of Adam and Eve.

The name of a province in Canada whose chief industry is agriculture.

A beast, but sacred to some.

A tract of land set apart for the benefit of the public.

One of the most important cities of China.

This will put a twinkle in her eye.

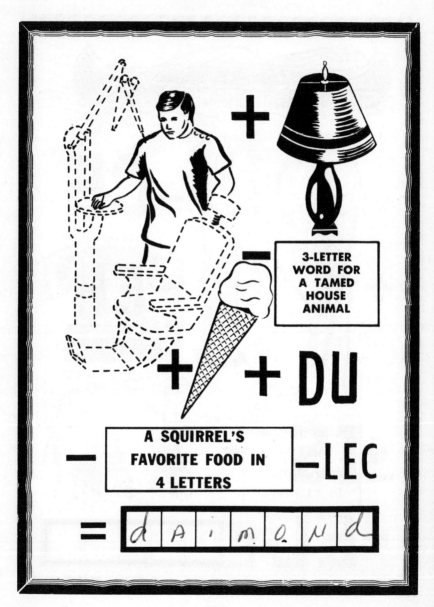

An organ in the body on which fat people
sometimes blame their overweight.

+ − EH

**Nickname
For Thomas
In 3 Letters**

+

**Affectionate
Term For
Your Mother
In 2 Letters**

−

−

= g l a n d

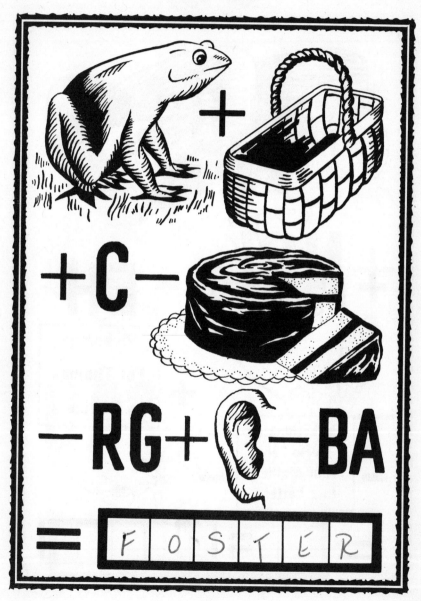

We have him to thank for several things it
would be hard to do without.

Solution is the name of a popular flavoring, and it's not chocolate.

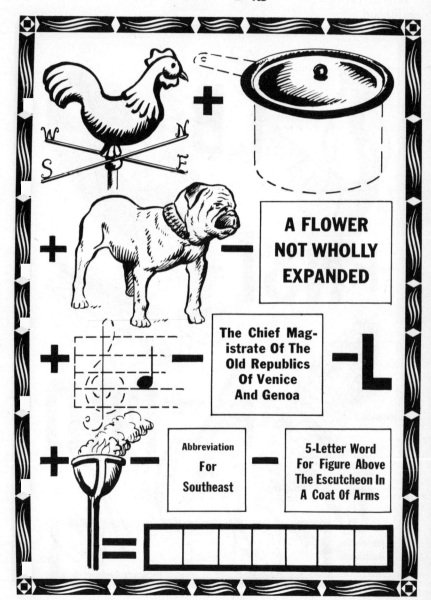

A Rhyme in Pictures

The picture puzzle below represents a rhyme you have known since childhood.

Whose Portraits Are On Your Money?

The following portraits are on the faces of U. S. currency as listed below:

Hamilton	Grant	Chase
Washington	Wilson	Madison
Lincoln	McKinley	Cleveland
Jackson	Franklin	

Insert in the box opposite each denomination the name of the man whose portrait is printed on its face:

$1	
$5	
$10	
$20	
$50	
$100	
$500	
$1,000	
$5,000	
$10,000	
$100,000	

(Yessir! You read right—we said a $100,000 bill!)

Correct Answers:

$1—Washington; $5—Lincoln; $10—Hamilton; $20—Jackson; $50—Grant; $100—Franklin; $500—McKinley; $1,000—Cleveland; $5,000—Madison; $10,000—Chase; $100,000—Wilson.

Which is the Highest Point in the World?

Select the correct one from the following list:

Kilimanjaro	Mount Aconcagua
Mont Blanc	Mount Ararat
Matterhorn	Jungfrau
Mount Mc Kinley	Mount Logan
Mount Everest	Old Baldy

Correct answer:

Mount Everest (Asia)—elevation 29,002 feet.

Where is the Lowest Spot in the World?

Pick the right one from the following list:

Death Valley, California	Libyan Desert
Dead Sea	Lake Eyre, South Australia

Correct answer:

Dead Sea, Palestine. It is 1,286 feet below sea level.

133

How Deep is the Ocean?

Put a check mark in the appropriate square below:

The oceans of the world are

☐ 5
☐ 10
☐ 15
☐ 20

in number.

Correct answer:

There are 5 oceans: Pacific, Atlantic, Indian, Antarctic, Arctic.

Check "true" or "false" to the following statement:

The deepest place in the ocean yet found is off the Island of Mindanao, in the Philippines Archipelago, where a sounding of 35,400 feet has been reported.

☐ **TRUE**   ☐ **FALSE**

Correct answer:

TRUE

AUTHOR! AUTHOR!

Here are the 21 authors of the selections listed below:

Mark Twain	Fielding	Austen	Swift
Dickens	Melville	Sewell	Darwin
Hawthorne	Milton	Conrad	Homer
Balzac	Boccaccio	Tolstoy	Dante
Shakespeare	Vergil	Alcott	Gibbon
			Carroll

Insert the name of the appropriate author in the box opposite each selection:

Alice's Adventures in Wonderland [ ]

Paradise Lost [ ]

Huckleberry Finn [ ]

The Scarlet Letter [ ]

Droll Tales [ ]

Black Beauty [ ]

The Origin of Species [ ]

The Divine Comedy [ ]

Tale of Two Cities [ ]

Hamlet [ ]

The Rise and Fall of the Roman Empire [ ]

The Odyssey [ ]

Gulliver's Travels [ ]

Little Women [ ]

Moby Dick [ ]

Tom Jones [ ]

Aeneid [ ]

Pride and Prejudice [ ]

The Call of the Wild [ ]

War and Peace [ ]

The Decameron [ ]

(See correct answers on page 180)

Distances

Here are twenty figures representing distances in nautical miles from New York City to various ports:

3,310	600	12,523	1,973	3,293
9,788	10,584	1,399	3,948	10,593
9,824	697	1,186	2,047	5,753
6,801	9,942	9,700	11,365	6,542

Insert the correct distances from New York City (in nautical miles) to the 20 ports listed below:

Adelaide, Australia

Bordeaux, France

Cape of Good Hope

Calcutta, India

Hamilton, Bermuda

Shanghai, China

Halifax, Nova Scotia

Singapore

Melbourne, Australia

Havana, Cuba

San Juan, Puerto Rico

Murmansk, U.S.S.R.

Limon, Costa Rica

Yokohama, Japan

Vera Cruz, Mexico

Manila, P. I.

Montevideo, Uruguay

Tsingtao, China

Le Havre, France

Sitka, Alaska

Correct Answers:

Adelaide—9,788; Bordeaux—3,310; Calcutta—9,824; Cape of Good Hope—6,801; Havana—1,186; Halifax—600; Hamilton—697; Le Havre—3,293; Limon—2,047; Manila—11,365; Melbourne—9,942; Montevideo—5,753; Murmansk—3,948; San Juan—1,399; Shanghai—10,584; Singapore—12,523; Sitka—6,542; Tsingtao—10,593; Vera Cruz—1,973; Yokohama—9,700. (These distances are in nautical miles. Multiply by 1.15 for statute miles).

The World's Great Inventions

The following persons invented the inventions listed on the next two pages:

DIESEL (German)

FRANKLIN (U. S.)

APPERT (French)

MOORE (U. S.)

WATERMAN (U. S.)

Mc CORMICK (U. S.)

ROENTGEN (German)

MEGE-MOURIES (French)

HOWE (U. S.)

LONG (U. S.)

GATLING (U. S.)

HILLS (U. S.)

NOBEL (Swedish)

OTIS (U. S.)

BAEKELAND (Belgian)

TORRICELLI (Italian)

GALILEO (Italian)

HOLT (U. S.)

MORSE (U. S.)

HUNT (U.S.)

GOODYEAR (U. S.)

BENZ (German)

HOE (U. S.)

BERLINER (U. S.)

WHITNEY (U. S.)

WALTON (English)

WRIGHT BROS. (U. S.)

EDISON (U. S.)

LAENNEC (French)

THOMPSON (U. S.)

MARCONI (Italian)

COLT (U. S.)

MERGENTHALER (U. S.)

FAHRENHEIT (German)

BELL (U. S.)

MAXIM (U. S.)

BUNSEN (German)

MITTERHOFFER (Austrian)

BAIRD (Scottish)

RITTY (U. S.)

WHITEHEAD (English)

BRANDENBERGER (French)

CRISTOFORI (Italian)

Insert the name of the inventor in the box opposite each invention below (names of inventors are listed on page 137):

Cotton Gin

Diesel Engine

Television

Elevator

Airplane (motor driven)

X-Ray

Telephone

Harvester

Tire (pneumatic)

Pistol (revolver)

Reaper

Motion Picture Machine

Lawn Mower

Automobile Engine
    (2-stroke)

Incandescent Lamp

Piano

Oleomargarine

Dynamite

Lightning Rod

Ether (as anaesthetic)

Food Preservation
    (by sterilization and
    exclusion of air)

(continued on next page)

Insert the name of the inventor opposite each invention below (names of inventors are listed on page 137):

Invention	Inventor
Cash Register	
Linoleum	
Cellophane	
Barometer	
Linotype	
Gas Burner	
Torpedo (self-propelled)	
Thermometer (mercurial)	
Stethoscope	
Bakelite	
Safety Pin	
Printing Press (rotary)	
Wireless Telegraph (high frequency)	
Tractor (caterpillar)	
Fountain Pen	
Rubber (vulcanized)	
Machine Gun	
Sewing Machine	
Typewriter	
Silencer	
Telegraph (magnetic)	
Microphone	
Pendulum	

(See pages 181 and 182 for correct answers)

Art Treasures

Which artists executed these famous paintings and statues? (Fill in your answer in the box opposite each of the following):

1—MONA LISA

2—THE LAST SUPPER

3—THE BLUE BOY

4—MOSES

5—VENUS DE MILO

6—APOLLO BELVEDERE

7—VICTORY OF
    SAMOTHRACE

8—PORTRAIT OF THE
    ARTIST'S MOTHER

9—THE THREE GRACES

10—THE LAST JUDGMENT

11—ANATOMY LECTURE

12—MADONNA DI TEMPI

Correct Answers:

1—Da Vinci; 2—Da Vinci; 3—Gainsborough; 4—Michelangelo; 5—Unknown; 6—Unknown; 7—Unknown; 8—Whistler; 9—Sargent; 10—Michelangelo; 11—Rembrandt; 12—Raphael.

Nobel Prizes for Literature Won by Americans

The Nobel Prize for literature has been awarded to five Americans.

Pick them out from this list:

Thomas Wolfe	Damon Runyon
Edna Ferber	Edith Wharton
O. Henry	John Steinbeck
Sinclair Lewis	John P. Marquand
John Dos Passos	Ellen Glasgow
Theodore Dreiser	Pearl Buck
Willa Cather	Thomas Costain
Conrad Aiken	William Faulkner
Eugene O'Neill	T. S. Eliot
Booth Tarkington	Henry James
Ernest Hemingway	Robert E. Sherwood
Mark Twain	Francis Bret Harte
Erskine Caldwell	Elbert Hubbard
Zona Gale	Edgar Allan Poe
Zane Grey	Kate Douglas Wiggin

Answers below:

Sinclair Lewis; Eugene O'Neill; Pearl Buck; T. S. Eliot; William Faulkner.

How Much Above Par Are You?

ANTIDISESTABLISHMENTARIAN-ISM is the longest nontechnical word in the English language.

How many words can you make out of it?

Listed below are 100 words, all made out of *ANTIDISESTABLISHMENT-ARIANISM*.

Par is 100. See how many *over* par *you* can figure out.

---

able	blind	heel	mind
air	bliss	hinder	mite
art	bread	hiss	missile
bad	bride	lad	rail
bait	bridle	lair	ran
ban	dame	lamb	rate
band	dander	last	rattle
bane	dear	late	read
banish	deer	leader	real
banister	den	leer	ream
banter	die	list	red
bar	dim	litter	rest
bare	dime	mare	rind
barn	din	mart	said
batter	distant	mat	salt
battle	ear	matter	sand
beam	enmesh	mean	satiate
bear	establishment	meander	seer
bed	hail	meat	shad
beet	hand	men	shame
bind	hate	mental	sidle
blandishments	hear	mesh	sled
blare	heart	medal	star
bleat	heat	metal	testament
bled	heed	mild	trestle

Wise Men's Sayings

On the following six pages, you will find a number of proverbs which we have puzzleized by means of pictures, letters, symbols, definitions, etc. These are picture puzzles, rather than strict rebus puzzles.

For correct solutions, see pages 183 and 184.

Poor Man's Dish Of Ground-Up And Cooked Left-over Meat –HH

U

M+

–R

Y+ PERIOD OF 60 MINUTES –H

SO

+ ABBREVIATION FOR STREET –G

U

AN UNTRUTH

Opposite of LOSE –W

–H

=

☐☐ ☐☐ ☐☐☐ ☐☐☐ ☐☐

☐☐ ☐☐☐ ☐☐☐ ☐☐☐ ☐☐ ☐☐

144

A  **Opposite** of **OUT**

 **TO** — **TEAR** —**C** In 3 Letters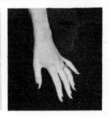

Singular of **ARE**   5-Letter Noun Meaning *The Value of Something*   **2**

Opposite of **SUMMER** —**WER** +  —**AD**   **BUSH**

=

☐ ☐☐☐☐ ☐☐ ☐☐☐ ☐☐☐☐ ☐☐

☐☐☐☐☐ ☐☐☐ ☐☐ ☐☐☐ ☐☐☐☐

Capital + of -R ITALY

-FH

ABBREVIATION ▬ FOR MOUNTAIN

ABBREVIATION + FOR NORTH DAKOTA -M+ FIRST WORD IN SOPHIE TUCKER'S MOST POPULAR SONG

=

☐☐☐☐☐☐☐☐ ☐☐ ☐☐

☐☐☐☐☐☐☐☐ ☐☐☐☐

T+  −N   **Opposite of LATE**

 +S−R

 − LIMB    +M

=

☐☐☐ ☐☐☐☐☐ ☐☐☐☐

☐☐☐☐☐☐ ☐☐☐ ☐☐☐☐

A LOT OF NOISE, −D
In 3 Letters

ABBREVIATION + FOR STREET

&

RE+  +T

 −H

 −  +  + RESTORE TO HEALTH, −PDHC
In 4 Letters

=

☐☐☐☐☐ ☐☐ ☐☐☐☐☐ ☐☐☐

☐☐☐☐☐☐ ☐☐ ☐☐☐☐☐☐

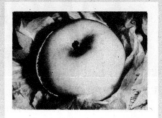

ABBREVIATION FOR
TERRITORY **+E**
OF HAWAII

D+  **-B**

  Opposite
of
NEAR

 **+M-G** **THE**

Bz-z-z

=

☐☐ ☐☐☐☐ ☐☐☐☐ ☐☐☐

☐☐☐☐ ☐☐☐ ☐☐☐☐ ☐☐☐ ☐☐☐☐

FAMOUS PEOPLE

How many of these outstanding persons can you recognize? Each of them is famous for an important reason or reasons.

The clue to their identity is below each picture.

You will find them identified by number on page 179.

1.

Teacher of Alexander, this great Greek shares with Plato the distinction of being the most famous of ancient philosophers.

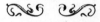

2.

This Greek statesman was responsible for an age which became known as the "Golden Age".

4.

A great Roman general and statesman, he fell in love with Cleopatra, and was immortalized by Shakespeare.

3.

This Queen of Egypt was the mother of children by two famous fathers. She committed suicide by the bite of a venomous serpent.

5.

One of the all-time artist "greats", this Renaissance Italian was sculptor, painter, architect and poet, and creator of incomparable masterpieces.

6.

Considered one of the geniuses of the world, this Italian artist excelled in the fields of painting, sculpture, architecture and engineering.

8.

Today his portrait master-pieces hang in museums and in value exceed many kings' ransoms, but this Dutch paint-er died in poverty in 1669.

7.

An English scientist who dis-covered an important law when an apple fell off a tree and hit him on the head.

Born in 1685 and known as the "daddy" of the world's musical greats, this famous German composer had 20 children.

9.

Famous for his religious paintings, especially his Madonnas, this Italian is a bright star in the firmament of greatest artists the world has known.

11.

A titan of music, this composer's Fifth Symphony furnished the theme for the Allied "Victory" musical motif of World War II.

12.

This musical "great" was a boy wonder who started writing compositions for the piano when he was four years old.

14.

Harsh and ruthless, but exceedingly shrewd and competent, this Queen worked relentlessly for the aggrandizement of her kingdom and thereby won the wholehearted esteem and love of her people.

13.

A famous German operatic composer, this famous man married his best friend's wife.

16.

This German poet and dramatist chose Faust as the princi-
pal character of one of his
most famous writings.

15.

Regarded by many as the fore-
most dramatist the world has
ever produced, this English
writer chose Italy as the locale
of many of his plays.

17.

This famous general, considered one of the greatest of
military geniuses, rose to be
Emperor of France but met
his defeat at Waterloo.

18.

*This English surgeon intro-
duced antiseptic surgery by
the chemical treatment of sep-
tic infections.*

20.

*Considered the greatest com-
poser of music for the piano,
this genius was born in Poland
but spent most of his adult life
in France, where he died at an
early age.*

19.

*Author of "The Scarlet Let-
ter", this American writer
made his mark as one of our
greatest novelists.*

22.

A great figure in American history, this man was printer, writer, patriot, statesman, and scientist.

21.

This French scientist developed a method of inhibiting fermentation of milk which has been named after him.

23.

Some of this French painter's works now hang in art museums, but his revolutionary new technique first earned him only scorn.

24.

Posterity considers him a genius among artists, but this painter led a pitifully unhappy life and cut off his own ear before being incarcerated for madness.

26.

All of his biographers have attested to the indestructible courage, sound judgment and absolute integrity of this famous American Revolutionary general and statesman.

25.

One of the signers of the Declaration of Independence, this great American statesman later became President.

28.

Together with her French husband, this Polish-born scientist discovered radium.

27.

This English naturalist wrote "The Origin of Species" *and formulated the theory of the survival of the fittest.*

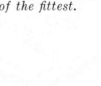

29.

One of the most beloved storytellers in history, this English writer created Scrooge, David Copperfield, Micawber, and other famous characters of fiction.

30.

This Russian aristocrat wrote "War and Peace", considered by many the greatest novel ever written.

31.

This political reformer, who lived in personal austerity, was instrumental in achieving the political independence of his native land, India.

32.

Their first names were Orville and Wilbur, and these two brothers were American aeronautic inventors.

34.

An American electrician and inventor, he perfected the incandescent lamp and invented the phonograph. He patented over 1,000 inventions.

33.

Not too many persons today have actually seen her emote, but this French actress still bears the reputation of one of the greatest tragedians of all time.

35.

An American writer and humorist, and creator of beloved fictional characters such as Tom Sawyer and Huckleberry Finn. He assumed a pen name.

Solutions to Rebus Puzzles

(from pages 1 to 130)

(from page 1)
Correct solution **BING**. To solve puzzle, write down COMBS. *Add* ITL, making COMBSITL. *Add* STOCKING, making COMBSITLSTOCKING. *Subtract* CLOCK, leaving MBSITSTOING. *Add* LEE (last name of an American Confederate Army General whose first two initials were R. E.), making MBSITSTOINGLEE. *Subtract* S, leaving MBITSTOINGLEE. *Subtract* MISTLETOE, leaving **BING**.

(from page 2)
Correct solution **DURANTE**. To solve puzzle, write down BRASSARD. *Add* IDO, making BRASSARDIDO. *Add* JANUARY (first month of the year), making BRASSARDIDOJANUARY. *Add* N, making BRASSARDIDOJANUARYN. *Add* CASTANETS, making BRASSARDIDOJANUARYNCASTANETS. *Subtract* ANDIRONS, leaving BSARDJAUARYCASTANETS. *Subtract* BEARS, leaving DJAUARYCASTANTS. *Subtract* CATS, leaving DJUARYAANTS. *Subtract* JAY (last name of first Chief Justice of the United States Supreme Court), leaving DURAANTS. *Subtract* AS, leaving DURANT. *Add* E, making **DURANTE**.

(from page 3)
Correct solution **ZIP**. To solve puzzle, write down ZIPPER. *Add* RAKES, making ZIPPERRAKES. *Add* NS, making ZIPPERRAKESNS. *Subtract* SNEAKER, leaving ZIPPRS. *Subtract* PRS (abbreviation for PAIRS), leaving **ZIP**.

(from page 4)
Correct solution **ADAMS**. To solve puzzle, write down PARACHUTE. *Add* KN, making PARACHUTEKN. *Subtract* TRUCK, leaving PAAHEN. *Subtract* EH, leaving PAAN. *Subtract* PAN, leaving A. *Add* DIAL, making ADIAL. *Add* MS, making ADIALMS. *Subtract* LI, leaving **ADAMS**.

(from page 5)
Correct solution **JERRY**. To solve puzzle, write down JUDGE. *Add* BIB, making JUDGEBIB. *Add* RTF, making JUDGEBIBRTF. *Subtract* BRIDGE, leaving JUBTF. *Subtract* TUB, leaving JF. *Add* CHERRY, making JFCHERRY. *Add* FA, making JFCHERRYFA. *Subtract* CHAFF (husks of grains and grasses separated from the seeds), leaving **JERRY**.

(from page 6)
Correct solution **TREE**. To solve puzzle, write down PDQ (3-letter slang expression for ON THE DOUBLE). *Add* SCOOTER, making PDQSCOOTER. *Add* EYE, making PDQSCOOTEREYE. *Subtract* SCOOP, leaving DQTEREYE. *Add* URN, making DQTEREYEURN. *Subtract* DRN, leaving QTEEYEUR. *Add* NURSE, making QTEEYEURNURSE. *Subtract* QUEUE, leaving TYERNRSE. *Add* OE, making TYERNRSEOE. *Subtract* ROSE, leaving TYNREE. *Subtract* NY, leaving **TREE**.

(from page 7)
Correct solution **MACY'S**. To solve puzzle, write down MERMAID. *Add* CFS, making MERMAIDCFS. *Add* CURIE (last name of co-discoverers of radium), making MERMAIDCFSCURIE. *Add* EYEBROWS, making MER-

162

MAIDCFSCURIEEYEBROWS. *Subtract* COW, leaving MERMAIDFSCURIEEYEBRS. *Subtract* BEE, leaving MRMAIDFSCURIEYERS. *Subtract* RR (abbreviation for railroad), leaving MMAIDFSCUIEYERS. *Subtract* DIME, leaving MAFSCUIYERS. *Add* ET, making MAFSCUIYERSET. *Subtract* FUSE, leaving MACIYRSET. *Subtract* TIRE, leaving **MACY'S.**

(from page 8)
Correct solution **JOE.** To solve puzzle, write down FAUCET. *Add* SCALE, making FAUCETSCALE. *Add* HJM, making FAUCETSCALEHJM. *Subtract* HELMET, leaving FAUCSCAJ. *Add* FP, making FAUCSCAJFP. *Subtract* CUFF, leaving ASCAJP. *Add* DOVE, making ASCAJPDOVE. *Subtract* VA (abbreviation for Virginia), leaving SCAJPDOE. *Subtract* CAPS, leaving JDOE. *Subtract* D, leaving **JOE.**

(from page 9)
Correct solution **WORLD SERIES.** To solve puzzle, write down WOMBAT. *Subtract* BAT, leaving WOM. *Add* RILEY (last name of American known as the "Hoosier Poet"), making WOMRILEY. *Add* E, making WOMRILEYE. *Subtract* EYE, leaving WOMRIL. *Add* DTT, making WOMRILDTT. *Subtract* MITT, leaving **WORLD.** Now write down SEPTEMBER (ninth month of the year). *Add* SE, making SEPTEMBERSE. *Add* DRUM, making SEPTEMBERSEDRUM. *Add* LY, making SEPTEMBERSEDRUMLY. *Subtract* M, leaving SEPTEBERSEDRUMLY. *Subtract* TUMBREL, leaving SPEESEDRY. *Subtract* SPEEDY (synonym for swift or rapid), leaving SER. *Add* DICE, making SERDICE. *Add* S, making SERDICES. *Subtract* DC (abbreviation for District of Columbia), leaving **SERIES.** Complete solution is **WORLD SERIES.**

(from page 10)
Correct solution **ALY KHAN.** To solve puzzle, write down BINNACLE. *Add* TB (slang for tuberculosis), making BINNACLETB. *Subtract* BIN, leaving NACLETB. *Subtract* CENT (1/100th of one dollar), leaving ALB. *Add* YKH, making ALBYKH. *Add* BASSOON, making ALBYKHBASSOON. *Subtract* BOB (abbreviation for Robert in 3 letters), leaving ALYKHASSON. *Subtract* SOS (international Call of Distress by ships at sea), leaving **ALY KHAN.**

(from page 11)
Correct solution **TALLULAH.** To solve puzzle, write down TEE. *Add* AMARYLLIS, making TEEAMARYLLIS. *Subtract* YEAR (period of 365 days), leaving TEMALLIS. *Add* C, making TEMALLISC. *Subtract* ICE, leaving TMALLS. *Add* BUOY, making TMALLSBUOY. *Add* LA (abbreviation for Los Angeles), making TMALLSBUOYLA. *Add* H, making TMALLSBUOYLAH. *Subtract* BOY (a male child), leaving TMALLSULAH. *Subtract* MS, leaving **TALLULAH.**

(from page 12)
Correct solution **ANNIE.** To solve puzzle, write down DANDELION. *Add* N, making DANDELIONN. *Subtract* LION, leaving DADENN. *Add* SIEVE, making DADENNSIEVE. *Add* T, making DADENNSIEVET. *Subtract* VEST, leaving DADNNIEE. *Subtract* DDE, leaving **ANNIE.**

(from page 13)
Correct solution **MOTHER.** To solve puzzle, write down MARCH (3rd month of the year). *Subtract* ARCH, leaving M. *Add* COT, making MCOT. *Add* HERS (opposite of HIS), making MCOTHERS. *Subtract* SC (abbreviation for South Carolina), leaving **MOTHER.**

(from page 14)
Correct solution **TIP.** To solve puzzle, write down AMBULANCE. *Add* LHA, making AMBULANCELHA. *Subtract*

ALULA, leaving MBNCEHA. *Subtract* BENCH, leaving MA. *Add* TEL, making MATEL. *Add* WHIP, making MATELWHIP. *Subtract* WHALE, leaving MTIP. *Subtract* M, leaving TIP.

(from page 15)
Correct solution **NELSON**. To solve puzzle, write down NEEDLE. *Add* CYSTOSCOPE, making NEEDLE-CYSTOSCOPE. *Subtract* COOP, leaving NEEDLEYSTSCE. *Add* RB, making NEEDLEYSTSCERB. *Subtract* TREY (three in cards or dice), leaving NEDLESSCEB. *Subtract* BED, leaving NLESSCE. *Subtract* SEC (abbreviation for Securities Exchange Commission), leaving NLSE. *Add* LS, making NLSELS. *Add* TON (2,000 lbs.), making NLSELSTON. *Subtract* TLS, leaving **NELSON**.

(from page 16)
Correct solution **SLEEP**. To solve puzzle, write down BANANA. *Add* SSK, making BANANASSK. *Add* KETTLE, making BANANASSKKETTLE. *Subtract* BASKET, leaving NANASKTLE. *Add* EPP, making NANASKTLEEPP. *Subtract* NAP (3-letter verb meaning TO HAVE A SHORT DOZE), leaving NASKTLEEP. *Subtract* TANK, leaving **SLEEP**.

(from page 17)
Correct solution **JINX**. To solve puzzle, write down CHECKERBOARD. *Add* SJ, making CHECKERBOARDSJ. *Add* SPHINX, making CHECKERBOARDSJSPHINX. *Subtract* SHEPHERD, leaving CCKBOARJSINX. *Subtract* ROCKS, leaving CBAJINX. *Subtract* CAB, leaving **JINX**.

(from page 18)
Correct solution **STASSEN**. To solve puzzle, write down CHRISTMAS (synonym for YULETIDE). *Add* MONEY (5-letter word for which the slang expression is moola or folding stuff), making CHRISTMASMONEY. *Subtract* CHIMNEY, leaving RSTASMO. *Add* EE, making RSTASMOEE. *Subtract* ROME (capital of Italy), leaving STASE. *Add* SEVEN (7), making STASESEVEN. *Subtract* EVE (the first woman), leaving **STASSEN**.

(from page 19)
Correct solution **HUG**. To solve puzzle, write down MICROPHONE. *Subtract* N, leaving MICROPHOE. *Add* CACTUS, making MICROPHOE-CACTUS. *Subtract* MICROSCOPE, leaving HACTU. *Subtract* CAT, leaving HU. *Add* G, making **HUG**.

(from page 20)
Correct solution **TNT**. To solve puzzle, write down HAT. *Add* CONCERTINA, making HATCONCERTINA. *Add* POT, making HATCONCERTINAPOT. *Add* RUM (3-letter alcoholic liquor usually distilled from molasses), making HATCONCERTINAPOTRUM. *Subtract* CORNUCOPIA, leaving HTETNATRM. *Subtract* MEAT (the flesh of animals as used for food), leaving HTNTR. *Subtract* HR, leaving **TNT**.

(from page 21)
Correct solution **CHARITY**. To solve puzzle, write down BUSKINS. *Add* HC, making BUSKINSHC. *Subtract* CHUB, leaving SKINS. *Add* CHARIOT, making SKINSCHARIOT. *Add* UT, making SKINSCHARIOTUT. *Subtract* TUSK, leaving INSCHARIOT. *Add* YE, making INSCHARIOTYE. *Subtract* NOSE (the part of the face which contains the nostrils), leaving ICHARITY. *Subtract* I, leaving **CHARITY**.

(from page 22)
Correct solution **LIE**. To solve puzzle, write down L. *Add* COLLIE, making

LCOLLIE. *Add* BAR, making LCOL-
LIEBAR. *Subtract* COLLAR, leaving
LIEB. *Add* BARGE, making LIEB-
BARGE. *Subtract* BBG, leaving LIE-
ARE. *Add* R, making LIEARER.
Subtract REAR (the hindmost or back
part of anything), leaving **LIE.**

(from page 23)
Correct solution **YANKS.** To solve
puzzle, write down ALY (first name
of Rita Hayworth's present husband).
Add FOOT, making ALYFOOT. *Add*
TANKS, making ALYFOOTTANKS.
Add LB (abbreviation for POUND
AV.), making ALYFOOTTANKSLB.
Subtract FOOTBALL, leaving
YTANKS. *Subtract* T, leaving
YANKS.

(from page 24)
Correct solution **MAY.** To solve puzzle, write down BRAZIL (largest republic of South America, whose capital is Rio de Janeiro). *Add* HM,
making BRAZILHM. *Add* LAFAY-
ETTE (last name of French General
who served in American Revolutionary
army), making BRAZILHMLAFAY-
ETTE. *Subtract* RLA, leaving BZIH-
MLAFAYETTE. *Subtract* ELIZA-
BETH (English Queen who was the
daughter of Henry VIII), leaving MF-
AYT. *Subtract* TF, leaving **MAY.**

(from page 25)
Correct solution **FAT.** To solve puzzle,
write down FLASK. *Add* MAT, making FLASKMAT. *Subtract* MASK,
leaving FLAT. *Add* OD (abbreviation
for OFFICER OF THE DAY), making FLATOD. *Add* L, making FLAT-
ODL. *Subtract* DOLL, leaving **FAT.**

(from page 26)
Correct solution **PATTON.** To solve
puzzle, write down PATCH. *Add*
SHORTS, making PATCHSHORTS.
Add ID, making PATCHSHORTSID.
Subtract SHIRT, leaving PACHOTSD.
Subtract HOD, leaving PACTS. *Add*
TONGS, making PACTSTONGS. *Sub-
tract* CGSS, leaving **PATTON.**

(from page 27)
Correct solution **NORTH.** To solve
puzzle, write down PEIGNOIR. *Sub-
tract* PIG, leaving ENOIR. *Add* L,
making ENOIRL. *Add* THIMBLE,
making ENOIRLTHIMBLE. *Subtract*
LIMB (4-letter noun for A LARGE
BRANCH OF A TREE), leaving
ENORTHILE. *Subtract* EEL, leaving
NORTHI. *Subtract* I. leaving **NORTH.**

(from page 28)
Correct solution **SPAT.** To solve puz-
zle, write down SPATULA. *Add*
BEET, making SPATULABEET. *Add*
LRD, making SPATULABEETLRD.
Subtract BEATER, leaving SPUL-
ATLD. *Subtract* DULL (adjective in
4 letters for NOT KEEN or NOT
SHARP), leaving **SPAT.**

(from page 29)
Correct solution **LOVERS.** To solve
puzzle, write down GLOVE. *Add*
DRAWERS, making GLOVEDRAW-
ERS. *Subtract* WAD (3-letter slang
word for a roll, as of paper money),
leaving GLOVERERS. *Subtract* GER
(first 3 letters in the name of a European republic, whose former capital
was Berlin), leaving **LOVERS.**

(from page 30)
Correct solution **CHOW.** To solve puz-
zle, write down CHAMPAGNE (9-
letter word for the queen of wines,
effervescent and usually white). *Add*
SNOWBALL, making CHAMPAGNE-
SNOWBALL. *Subtract* BALL, leav-
ing CHMPAGNESNOWA. *Subtract*
SAM (3-letter abbreviated form of
SAMUEL), leaving CHPGNENOWA.
Subtract PEN, leaving CHGNOWA.
Subtract AGN, leaving **CHOW.**

(from page 31)
Correct solution **GENTLEMAN.** To
solve puzzle, write down WIG. *Add*
KENTUCKY, making WIGKEN-
TUCKY. *Add* A, making WIGKEN-
TUCKYA. *Add* MO (abbreviation for
MONEY ORDER), making WIGKEN-
TUCKYAMO. *Add* SLED, making
WIGKENTUCKYAMOSLED. *Sub-*

165

tract D, leaving WIGKENTUCKY-AMOSLE. *Subtract* SMOCK, leaving WIGENTUKYALE. *Add* MAN (3-letter noun for a MALE ADULT), making WIGENT.UKYALEMAN. *Subtract* AUK, leaving WIGENTYLEMAN. *Subtract* YWI, leaving **GENTLEMAN.**

(from page 32)
Correct solution **BIBLE.** To solve puzzle, write down BLACKBOARD. *Subtract* BLACK (opposite of WHITE), leaving BOARD. *Add* OW, making BOARDOW. *Subtract* DOOR, leaving BAW. *Subtract* A, leaving BW. *Add* TIMETABLE, making BWTIMETABLE. *Subtract* MAT, leaving BWIETBLE. *Subtract* WET (synonym for MOIST), leaving **BIBLE.**

(from page 33)
Correct solution **REMBRANDT.** To solve puzzle, write down FIREMAN. *Subtract* FAN, leaving IREM. *Add* B, making IREMB. *Add* PRAWN, making IREMBPRAWN. *Add* CUPID, making IREMBPRAWNCUPID. *Add* T, making IREMBPRAWNCUPIDT. *Subtract* CUP, leaving IREMBRAWNPIDT. *Subtract* PW (abbreviation for PRISONER OF WAR), leaving IREMBRANIDT. *Subtract* I, leaving REMBRANIDT. *Subtract* I (ninth letter of English alphabet), leaving **REMBRANDT.**

(from page 34)
Correct solution **ALWAYS.** To solve puzzle, write down OVERALLS. *Add* T, making OVERALLST. *Subtract* STOVE, leaving RALL. *Add* WEN, making RALLWEN. *Add* DIARY, making RALLWENDIARY. *Add* SOFT (opposite of HARD), making RALLWENDIARYSOFT. *Subtract* OFTEN (opposite of SELDOM), leaving RALLWDIARYS. *Subtract* LID, leaving RALWARYS. *Subtract* RR (abbreviation for RAILROAD), leaving **ALWAYS.**

(from page 35)
Correct solution **HUSH.** To solve puzzle, write down FAUCET. *Add* SOAP, making FAUCETSOAP. *Add* HO, making FAUCETSOAPHO. *Add* BRUSH, making FAUCETSOAPHOBRUSH. *Add* ZRR, making FAUCETSOAPHOBRUSHZRR. *Subtract* RAZOR, leaving FUCETSAPHOBUSHR. *Subtract* STROP, leaving FUCEAHBUSH. *Subtract* UEF, leaving CAHBUSH. *Subtract* CAB, leaving **HUSH.**

(from page 36)
Correct solution **OK.** To solve puzzle, write down REFRIGERATOR. *Add* T, making REFRIGERATORT. *Subtract* TARGET, leaving FRIEROR. *Subtract* I, leaving FREROR. *Add* DOME, making FRERORDOME. *Subtract* FREEDOM (noun meaning the OPPOSITE OF SLAVERY OR BONDAGE), leaving RRO. *Subtract* RR (abbreviation for RAILROAD), leaving O. *Add* K, making **OK.**

(from page 37)
Correct solution **STALIN.** To solve puzzle, write down CRESCENT. *Add* AI, making CRESCENTAI. *Add* ALB, making CRESCENTAIALB. *Subtract* CARIBE, leaving SCENTAL. *Subtract* NC (abbreviation for North Carolina), leaving SETAL. *Add* FIN, making SETALFIN. *Subtract* FE, leaving **STALIN.**

(from page 38)
Correct solution **COLUMBUS.** To solve puzzle, write down BROCCOLI. *Subtract* COB, leaving RCOLI. *Add* GUM (3-letter noun meaning a flavored substance chewed by many Americans, sometimes producing bubbles), making RCOLIGUM. *Add* SB, making RCOLIGUMSB. *Add* FUSE, making RCOLIGUMSBFUSE. *Subtract* FIGS, leaving RCOLUMBUSE. *Subtract* RE, leaving **COLUMBUS.**

(from page 39)
Correct solution **LAUGHTER**. To solve puzzle, write down LILY. *Add* SAD (opposite of GLAD), making LILYSAD. *Subtract* DAISY, leaving LL. *Add* ES, making LLES. *Add* DAUGHTER (a man's FEMALE CHILD), making LLESDAUGHTER. *Subtract* SLED, leaving **LAUGHTER**.

(from page 40)
Correct solution **JACK**. To solve puzzle, write down JACKET. *Add* TENT, making JACKETTENT. *Add* KL, making JACKETTENTKL. *Subtract* KETTLE, leaving JACNTK. *Add* SE (abbreviation for SOUTHEAST), making JACNTKSE. *Subtract* NEST, leaving **JACK**.

(from page 41)
Correct solution **TRUMAN**. To solve puzzle, write down CENTAUR. *Add* UP (opposite of down), making CENTAURUP. *Subtract* PANE, leaving CTURU. *Add* CAMELLIA, making CTURUCAMELLIA. *Add* BHN, making CTURUCAMELLIABHN. *Subtract* CHUB, leaving TRUCAMELLIAN. *Subtract* CELL, leaving TRUAMIAN. *Subtract* AI, leaving **TRUMAN**.

(from page 42)
Correct solution **EISENHOWER**. To solve puzzle, write down CONCERTINA. *Add* IBS, making CONCERTINAIBS. *Subtract* CRAB, leaving ONCETINIS. *Add* BEACON, making ONCETINISBEACON. *Add* HNRH, making ONCETINISBEACONHNRH. *Add* CROW, making ONCETINISBEACONHNRHCROW. *Add* BADGER, making ONCETINISBEACONHNRHCROWBADGER. *Subtract* BIGHORN, leaving CETNISEACONNHCROWBADER. *Subtract* BAD (opposite of good in 3 letters), leaving CETNISECONNHCROWAER. *Subtract* C, leaving ETNISECONNHCROWAER. *Subtract* CARTON, leaving EISENNHCOWER. *Subtract* NC (abbreviation for North Carolina), leaving **EISENHOWER**.

(from page 43)
Correct solution **QUEEN**. To solve puzzle, write down TOURNIQUET. *Add* PEW, making TOURNIQUETPEW. *Add* SECOND (1/60th of one minute), making TOURNIQUETPEWSECOND. *Subtract* TOWER, leaving UNIQUTPESECOND. *Add* AND, making UNIQUTPESECONDAND. *Subtract* COAT, leaving UNIQUPESENDND. *Subtract* DDS (abbreviation for DOCTOR OF DENTAL SURGERY), leaving UNIQUPEENN. *Subtract* PIN, leaving UQUEENN. *Subtract* UN (abbreviation for UNITED NATIONS), leaving **QUEEN**.

(from page 44)
Correct solution **PLEASE**. To solve puzzle, write down PLOW. *Add* DOWEL. making PLOWDOWEL. *Subtract* OWL, leaving PDOWEL. *Add* CLOWN, making PDOWELCLOWN. *Add* TREE, making PDOWELCLOWNTREE. *Subtract* TOWEL, leaving PDCLOWNREE. *Add* BOW, making PDCLOWNREEBOW. *Add* ASE, making PDCLOWNREEBOWASE. *Subtract* ROW (slang for a noisy quarrel), leaving PDCLNEEBOWASE. *Subtract* BED, leaving PCLNEOWASE. *Subtract* C, leaving PLNEOWASE. *Subtract* NOW (opposite of THEN), leaving **PLEASE**.

(from page 45)
Correct solution **CANTOR**. To solve puzzle, write down CHANDELIER. *Subtract* DEER, leaving CHANLI. *Add* LTP, making CHANLILTP. *Subtract* HILL, (4-letter noun for an ELEVATION SMALLER THAN A MOUNTAIN), leaving CANTP. *Add* FORK, making CANTPFORK. *Subtract* KP (abbreviation for KITCHEN POLICE), leaving CANTFOR. *Subtract* F, leaving **CANTOR**.

(from page 46)
Correct solution **DODGERS**. To solve puzzle, write down D. *Add* CONDUCTOR, making DCONDUCTOR. *Add* EE, making DCONDUCTOREE. *Subtract* CONE, leaving DDUCTORE. *Subtract* CUE, leaving DDTOR. *Subtract* TR (initials of 26th President of United States), leaving DDO. *Add* D, making DDOD. *Add* GARTERS, making DDODGARTERS. *Subtract* DART, leaving **DODGERS**.

(from page 47)
Correct solution **NYLON**. To solve puzzle, write down VAN. *Subtract* VA (abbreviation for VIRGINIA), leaving N. *Add* YLD, making NYLD. *Add* OHIO, making NYLDOHIO. *Add* N, making NYLDOHION. *Subtract* HOD, leaving NYLION. *Subtract* I, leaving **NYLON**.

(from page 48)
Correct solution **BUSHEL**. To solve puzzle, write down COLUMBUS (last name of the man who discovered America in 1492). *Subtract* LU, leaving COMBUS. *Add* RI (abbreviation for RHODE ISLAND), making COMBUSRI. *Add* NA (abbreviation for NORTH AMERICA), making COMBUSRINA. *Subtract* MARCONI (last name of the man who perfected wireless telegraphy), leaving BUS. *Add* HEL, making **BUSHEL**.

(from page 49)
Correct solution **REGIMENT**. To solve puzzle, write down GRAPES. *Add* GI (popular nickname in 2 letters for American soldier of World War II), making GRAPESGI. *Subtract* GAS (colloquial 3-letter word for GASOLINE), leaving RPEGI. *Add* MANY (opposite of FEW), making RPEGIMANY. *Subtract* PAN, leaving REGIMY. *Add* TENT, making REGIMYTENT. *Subtract* TY, leaving **REGIMENT**.

(from page 50)
Correct solution **NIXON**. To solve puzzle, write down BASINET. *Add* IF (conjunction meaning "in case that"), making BASINETIF. *Add* AXLE, making BASINETIFAXLE. *Subtract* LEAF, leaving BSINTIAXE. *Add* BAYONET, making BSINTIAXEBAYONET. *Subtract* BIT, leaving SNIAXEBAYONET. *Subtract* S, leaving NIAXEBAYONET. *Add* ERT, making NIAXEBAYONETERT. *Subtract* TRAY, leaving NIXEBAONEET. *Subtract* BEE, leaving NIXAONET. *Subtract* TEA (a somewhat bitter, aromatic beverage popular in England), leaving **NIXON**.

(from page 51)
Correct solution **MONEY**. To solve puzzle, write down MOCCASIN. *Add* JEANS, making MOCCASINJEANS. *Subtract* CIJ, leaving MOCASNEANS. *Add* TT, making MOCASNEANSTT. *Subtract* CASTANETS, leaving MON. *Add* E, making MONE. *Add* DAY (period of 24 HOURS), making MONEDAY. *Subtract* DA (abbreviation for DISTRICT ATTORNEY), leaving **MONEY**.

(from page 52)
Correct solution **TOM**. To solve puzzle, write down TRAILER. *Add* T, making TRAILERT. *Subtract* TAIL, leaving RERT. *Add* COMB, making RERTCOMB. *Subtract* BC, leaving RERTOM. *Subtract* ERR (3-letter verb meaning *to be mistaken or to stray*), leaving **TOM**.

(from page 53)
Correct solution **LIEDERKRANZ**. To solve puzzle, write down LIE (three-letter verb meaning to tell an untruth). *Add* DEAR (term of endearment, in 4 letters beginning with D), making LIEDEAR. *Add* KRAUT (World War II term applied by American soldiers to Germans, in 5 letters beginning

with K), making LIEDEARKRAUT. *Add* BNZ, making LIEDEARKRAUT-BNZ. *Subtract* TUB, leaving LIEDEARKRANZ. *Subtract* A, leaving **LIEDERKRANZ.**

(from page 54)
Correct solution **WINNIE.** To solve puzzle, write down WHITMAN (last name of American author who wrote "Leaves of Grass"). *Add* N, making WHITMANN. *Add* LISTER (last name of English surgeon who introduced antiseptic surgery), making WHITMANNLISTER. *Subtract* THAMES (name of the most important river in Great Britain which flows through London), leaving WINNLITR. *Add* E, making WINNLITRE. *Subtract* LTR, leaving **WINNIE.**

(from page 55)
Correct solution **COCKTAIL.** To solve puzzle, write down CLOCK. *Add* TABLE, making CLOCKTABLE. *Subtract* BELL, leaving COCKTA. *Add* SILL, making COCKTASILL. *Add* DD, making COCKTASILLDD. *Subtract* DDS (abbreviation for Doctor of Dental Surgery), leaving COCKTAILL. *Subtract* L, leaving **COCKTAIL.**

(from page 56)
Correct solution **EPSOM.** To solve puzzle, write down NET. *Add* EPITAPH, making NETEPITAPH. *Add* CISCO, making NETEPITAPHCISCO. *Add* LRK, making NETEPITAPHCISCOLRK. *Subtract* PICK, leaving NETETAPHISCOLR. *Subtract* CLARINET, leaving ETPHSO. *Add* DIR, making ETPHSODIR. *Subtract* THIRD (3rd), leaving EPSO. *Add* M, making **EPSOM.**

(from page 57)
Correct solution **DANCING.** To solve puzzle, write down DANE (a native of Denmark). *Add* CHIPMUNK, making DANECHIPMUNK. *Add* OSG, making DANECHIPMUNKOSG. *Subtract* MOP, leaving DANECHIUNKSG.

Subtract E, leaving DANCHIUNKSG. *Subtract* HUKS (current term to denote guerrilla fighters in modern Philippines), leaving **DANCING.**

(from page 58)
Correct solution **AUTRY.** To solve puzzle, write down LEOTARD. *Add* EPAULET, making LEOTARDEPAULET. *Subtract* LEOPARD, leaving TEAULET. *Add* RY (abbreviation for RAILWAY), making TEAULETRY. *Subtract* TEE, leaving AULTRY. *Subtract* L, leaving **AUTRY.**

(from page 59)
Correct solution **HOME.** To solve puzzle, write down STETHOSCOPE. *Subtract* SCOOP (in journalistic slang, a 'story' beat), leaving TETHSE. *Add* O, making TETHSEO. *Add* AMICE, making TETHSEOAMICE. *Subtract* ST (abbreviation for street), leaving ETHEOAMICE. *Subtract* TEE, leaving HOAMICE. *Subtract* ICA, leaving **HOME.**

(from page 60)
Correct solution **FLORENCE.** To solve puzzle, write down HOSE. *Subtract* SHOE, leaving nothing. *Add* FLORIN (a former gold coin weighing about 55 grains, first issued at Florence in 1252), making FLORIN. *Subtract* IN (opposite of OUT), leaving FLOR. *Add* PENCE (the plural of an English bronze coin equal to 1/12th of one shilling), making FLORPENCE. *Subtract* P, leaving **FLORENCE.**

(from page 61)
Correct solution **MILLER.** To solve puzzle, write down POE (last name of American author who wrote "The Raven"). *Add* MILTON (last name of English poet who wrote "Paradise Lost"), making POEMILTON. *Add* ELEVEN (11), making POEMILTONELEVEN. *Add* USSR (abbreviation for UNION OF SOCIALIST

SOVIET REPUBLICS), making POEMILTONELEVENUSSR. *Subtract* STEVENSON (last name of English author of "Treasure Island"), leaving PMILOLEEUR. *Subtract* UP (opposite of DOWN), leaving MILOLEER. *Subtract* OE, leaving **MILLER.**

(from page 62)
Correct solution **TERRIBLE.** To solve puzzle, write down ATOMIZER. *Add* BBB, making ATOMIZERBBB. *Subtract* BOMB, leaving ATIZERB. *Subtract* ZEBRA, leaving TI. *Add* KETTLEDRUM, making TIKETTLEDRUM. *Subtract* MITT, leaving KETLEDRU. *Add* S, making KETLEDRUS. *Add* RIB, making KETLEDRUSRIB. *Subtract* SLED, leaving KTERURIB. *Add* LE, making KTERURIBLE. *Subtract* KU, leaving **TERRIBLE.**

(from page 63)
Correct solution **HUGHES.** To solve puzzle, write down WILLIAMS (last name of the man who founded the colony of Rhode Island). *Add* HUDSON (last name of the explorer who discovered an important river in New YORK state, after whom river was named), making WILLIAMSHUDSON. *Subtract* SA (abbreviation for SOUTH AMERICA), leaving WILLIMHUDSON. *Add* OLO, making WILLIMHUDSONOLO. *Subtract* SOLOMON (name of a Biblical King reputed to have 1,000 wives), leaving WILIHUDL. *Subtract* WILL (4-letter noun for LAST TESTAMENT), leaving IHUD. *Add* GHE, making IHUDGHE. *Subtract* DI, leaving HUGHE. *Add* S, making **HUGHES.**

(from page 64)
Correct solution **CHAMBERS.** To solve puzzle, write down CHAPS. *Subtract* PS (abbreviation for POSTSCRIPT), leaving CHA. *Add* M, making CHAM. *Add* BEER (a popular alcoholic beverage flavored with hops, and with a head on it when poured), making CHAMBEER. *Add* S, making CHAMBEERS. *Subtract* E, making **CHAMBERS.**

(from page 65)
Correct solution **BRUNCH.** To solve puzzle, write down NEAR (opposite of FAR). *Add* CARBOY, making NEARCARBOY. *Add* THP, making NEARCARBOYTHP. *Add* AMPHORA, making NEARCARBOYTHPAMPHORA. *Add* LOUISIANA, making NEARCARBOYTHPAMPHORALOUISIANA. *Subtract* PAR, leaving NECARBOYTHAMPHORALOUISIANA. *Add* DGS, making NECARBOYTHAMPHORALOUISIANADGS. *Subtract* MIDNIGHT (12 o'clock at night), leaving ECARBOYAPHORALOUSANAS. *Subtract* OAR, leaving ECBYAPHORALOUSANAS. *Subtract* SOAP, leaving ECBYHRALOUANAS. *Subtract* HOE, leaving CBYRALUANAS. *Subtract* ALAS (exclamation of sorrow in 4 letters), leaving CBYRUNA. *Add* CH, making CBYRUNACH. *Subtract* Y, leaving CBRUNACH. *Subtract* AC (abbreviation for Alternating Current), leaving **BRUNCH.**

(from page 66)
Correct solution **HETTY GREEN.** To solve puzzle, write down HANDLE. *Add* CS, making HANDLECS. *Add* TICKET, making HANDLECSTICKET. *Subtract* CANDLESTICK, leaving HET. *Add* TRY (3-letter verb meaning TO MAKE AN EFFORT or TO ATTEMPT), making HETTRY. *Add* GREEN (the color of grass), making HETTRYGREEN. *Subtract* R, leaving HETTY GREEN.

(from page 67)
Correct solution **LEE.** To solve puzzle, write down BLIND. *Add* PINEAPPLE, making BLINDPINEAPPLE. *Add* RE, making BLINDPINEAPPLERE. *Subtract* BARN, leaving

LIDPINEPPLEE. *Subtract* NIPPLE, leaving DPILEE. *Subtract* DIP, leaving **LEE.**

(from page 68)
Correct solution **DOG.** To solve puzzle, write down HANDLE. *Add* BROUGHAM, making HANDLEBROUGHAM. *Add* S, making HANDLEBROUGHAMS. *Subtract* HAM, leaving NDLEBROUGHAS. *Subtract* BRUSH, leaving NDLEOGA. *Subtract* LEA (poetic term in 3 letters for MEADOW), leaving NDOG. *Subtract* N, leaving **DOG.**

(from page 69)
Correct solution **PERRY.** To solve puzzle, write down ONION. *Add* P, making ONIONP. *Add* PLUMBER, making ONIONPPLUMBER. *Subtract* BUNION (6-letter noun meaning unsightly swelling on the foot, especially the big toe), leaving OPPLMER. *Add* A, making OPPLMERA. *Subtract* PALM, leaving OPER. *Add* RY, making OPERRY. *Subtract* O, leaving **PERRY.**

(from page 70)
Correct solution **BOOKIES.** To solve puzzle, write down BOOKS. *Add* SWATCH, making BOOKSSWATCH. *Add* NEST, making BOOKSSWATCHNEST. *Add* PRIDE (5-letter synonym for SELF-ESTEEM), making BOOKSSWATCHNESTPRIDE. *Subtract* WATCH, leaving BOOKSSNESTPRIDE. *Subtract* DRESS, leaving BOOKNSTPIE. *Add* SS (abbreviation for SHORTSTOP IN BASEBALL), making BOOKNSTPIESS. *Subtract* NTP, leaving BOOKSIESS. *Subtract* SS (first two initials of mystery writer Van Dine), leaving **BOOKIES.**

(from page 71)
Correct solution **LOMOND.** To solve puzzle, write down SLD. *Add* LOLLIPOP, making SLDLOLLIPOP. *Subtract* LIPS, leaving DLOLLOP. *Subtract* DOLL, leaving LOP. *Add* PIANISSIMO, making LOPPIANISSIMO. *Subtract* PAINS (synonym in 5 letters for ACHES), leaving LOPISIMO. *Add* ND (abbreviation for North Dakota), making LOPISIMOND. *Subtract* I, leaving LOPSIMOND. *Subtract* SIP (3-letter verb meaning to take up liquid with the lips in small quantities for swallowing), leaving **LOMOND.**

(from page 72)
Correct solution **GROCERIES.** To solve puzzle, write down GOAT. *Add* ROWBOAT, making GOATROWBOAT. *Subtract* BAT, leaving GOROWOAT. *Add* CHL, making GOROWOATCHL. *Subtract* COW, leaving GROOATHL. *Subtract* HAT, leaving GROOL. *Add* CELERY, making GROOLCELERY. *Subtract* YELL (4-letter verb meaning to CRY OUT WITH A LOUD SOUND), leaving GROOCER. *Add* PIES, making GROOCERPIES. *Subtract* PO (abbreviation for POST OFFICE), leaving **GROCERIES.**

(from page 73)
Correct solution **CODY.** To solve puzzle, write down SCHOOL. *Add* DIARY, making SCHOOLDIARY. *Subtract* LIAR (4-letter noun meaning a person who does not tell the truth), leaving SCHOODY. *Add* ER, making SCHOODYER. *Subtract* HORSE, leaving **CODY.**

(from page 74)
Correct solution **NO.** To solve puzzle, write down WATER. *Add* OXYGEN (a chemical element whose symbol is O), making WATEROXYGEN. *Add* JB, making WATEROXYGENJB. *Subtract* JAR, leaving WTEOXYGENB. *Subtract* EYE, leaving WTOXGNB. *Subtract* WTG, leaving OXNB. *Subtract* BOX, leaving N. *Add* O, making **NO.**

(from page 75)
Correct solution **BUTTER**. To solve puzzle, write down BURGEE. *Add* TC, making BURGEETC. *Add* TELLER, making BURGEETCTELLER. *Subtract* REEL, leaving BUGTCTELER. *Subtract* LEG, leaving BUTCTER. *Add* LOG, making BUTCTERLOG. *Subtract* COG, leaving BUTTERL. *Subtract* L, leaving **BUTTER**.

(from page 76)
Correct solution **GOUT**. To solve puzzle, write down LIGHTER. *Add* CIGAR, making LIGHTERCIGAR. *Add* POUCH, making LIGHTERCIGARPOUCH. *Add* EPM, making LIGHTERCIGARPOUCHEPM. *Subtract* PIPE, leaving LGHTRCIGAROUCHEM. *Add* TET, making LGHTRCIGAROUCHEMTET. *Subtract* CIGARETTE, leaving LHGROUCHMT. *Add* AT, making LHGROUCHMTAT. *Subtract* MATCH, leaving LGROUHT. *Subtract* HLR, leaving **GOUT**.

(from page 77)
Correct solution **LABRADOR**. To solve puzzle, write down KOHLRABI. *Add* RN (abbreviation for REGISTERED NURSE), making KOHLRABIRN. *Subtract* KNOB, leaving HLRAIR. *Add* BREAD, making HLRAIRBREAD. *Subtract* I, leaving HLRARBREAD. *Add* FOUR (4), making HLRARBREADFOUR. *Subtract* FUHRER (6-letter word which was applied by Germans to Hitler, meaning LEADER), leaving **LABRADOR**.

(from page 78)
Correct solution **HISS**. To solve puzzle, write down WATCH. *Add* CHIPS, making WATCHCHIPS. *Add* W, making WATCHCHIPSW. *Add* SON (a man's male child in 3 letters), making WATCHCHIPSWSON. *Subtract* CHOW, leaving ATCHIPSWSN. *Subtract* PAN, leaving TCHISWS. *Sub-* tract CWT (abbreviation for HUNDREDWEIGHT), leaving **HISS**.

(from page 79)
Correct solution **YALE**. To solve puzzle, write down MICHELANGELO (famous Italian Renaissance painter, sculptor, architect and poet, who decorated the Sistine Chapel with paintings that are world masterpieces). *Add* BIY, making MICHELANGELOBIY. *Subtract* BELL (last name of inventor of the telephone), leaving MICHANGEOIY. *Subtract* MICHIGAN (State of which Lansing is the capital), leaving EOY. *Add* ALE, making EOYALE. *Subtract* EO, leaving **YALE**.

(from page 80)
Correct solution **PARENTS**. To solve puzzle, write down SHAKESPEARE (last name of English writer, the greatest of dramatic poets, known as the "Bard of Avon"). *Add* W, making SHAKESPEAREW. *Subtract* SHAW (last name of Irish author who wrote "Candida"), leaving KESPEARE. *Subtract* SEEK (4-letter verb meaning to search for or look for), leaving PARE. *Add* NTS, making **PARENTS**.

(from page 81)
Correct solution **TWEED**. To solve puzzle, write down W. *Add* TWEEZERS, making WTWEEZERS. *Add* OL, making WTWEEZERSOL. *Subtract* ZERO (4-letter word for the figure or symbol 0, meaning NAUGHT), leaving WTWEESL. *Add* DRAGON, making WTWEESLDRAGON. *Subtract* WAGON, leaving TWEESLDR. *Subtract* RLS (initials of author of "TREASURE ISLAND"), leaving **TWEED**.

(from page 82)
Correct solution **FUR**. To solve puzzle, write down FRANKFURTER. *Add* MITT, making FRANKFURTERMITT. *Subtract* MINK (4-letter word for a fur, of a natural brown color,

much prized by women), leaving FRAFURTERTT. *Add* AW, making FRAFURTERTTAW. *Subtract* WATER, leaving FFURRTTA. *Subtract* RAT, leaving FFURT. *Subtract* TF, leaving **FUR**.

(from page 83)
Correct solution **CHICKEN**. To solve puzzle, write down CALASH. *Add* HICK (slang for an ignorant person from the country), making CALASHHICK. *Add* KA, making CALASHHICKKA. *Add* BLENNY, making CALASHHICKKABLENNY. *Subtract* NY (abbreviation for New York), leaving CALASHHICKKABLEN. *Subtract* ALASKA, leaving CHHICKBLEN. *Subtract* HBL, leaving **CHICKEN**.

(from page 84)
Correct solution **GONDOLA**. To solve puzzle, write down OREGON. *Add* ALF, making OREGONALF. *Subtract* OAR, leaving EGONLF. *Add* DOLL, making EGONLFDOLL. *Add* A, making EGONLFDOLLA. *Subtract* FELL, leaving **GONDOLA**.

(from page 85)
Correct solution **MILLS**. To solve puzzle, write down AUTOMOBILE. *Add* FL, making AUTOMOBILEFL. *Subtract* FOOTBALL, leaving UMIE. *Add* WILL, making UMIEWILL. *Add* SP, making UMIEWILLSP. *Subtract* PEW, leaving UMIILLS. *Subtract* IU, leaving **MILLS**.

(from page 86)
Correct solution **DEUCE**. To solve puzzle, write down CINCH (slang for something sure or easy). *Add* CADUCEUS, making CINCHCADUCEUS. *Add* BWT, making CINCHCADUCEUSBWT. *Subtract* BUS, leaving CINCHCADCEUWT. *Subtract* WINCH, leaving CCADCEUT. *Subtract* CCC (abbreviation for Civilian Conservation Corps), leaving ADEUT. *Subtract* A, leaving DEUT. *Add* CENT (1/100th of One Dollar), making DEUTCENT.

Subtract TNT (abbreviation for explosive called Trinitrotoluene), leaving **DEUCE**.

(from page 87)
Correct solution **LATE**. To solve puzzle, write down MAILBOX. *Add* ELEPHANT, making MAILBOXELEPHANT. *Add* RIS, making MAILBOXELEPHANTRIS. *Add* TONGUE, making MAILBOXELEPHANTRISTONGUE. *Subtract* EXTINGUISHER, leaving MALBOLPATONE. *Subtract* BOOM, leaving ALLPATNE. *Add* I, making ALLPATNEI. *Subtract* PAIL, leaving LATNE. *Subtract* N, leaving **LATE**.

(from page 88)
Correct solution **PYLE**. To solve puzzle, write down PLAYBILL. *Add* WASHBOARD, making PLAYBILLWASHBOARD. *Subtract* BILL, leaving PAYLWASHBOARD. *Subtract* BAR, leaving PYLWASHOAD. *Subtract* OD, leaving PYLWASHA. *Subtract* SHAW (last name of a famous Irish author and playwright whose initials are G. B. S.), leaving PYLA. *Add* E, making PYLAE. *Subtract* A, leaving **PYLE**.

(from page 89)
Correct solution **HST**. To solve puzzle, write down CHEF. *Add* LADLE, making CHEFLADLE. *Add* KB; making CHEFLADLEKB. *Subtract* CAKE, leaving HFLDLEB. *Subtract* BELL, leaving HFD. *Add* ST (abbreviation for SAINT), making HFDST. *Subtract* FD (abbreviation for FIRE DEPARTMENT), leaving **HST**.

(from page 90)
Correct solution **ARMY**. To solve puzzle, write down ARROW. *Subtract* RW, leaving ARO. *Add* BUMPER, making AROBUMPER. *Subtract* ER, leaving AOBUMPR. *Add* HOT (opposite of COLD), making AOBUMPR-

HOT. *Subtract* HOBO, leaving AUMPRT. *Add* HMY, making AUMPRTHMY. *Subtract* THUMP (5-letter verb meaning to STRIKE OR BEAT HEAVILY, WITH A DULL SOUND), leaving **ARMY**.

(from page 91)
Correct solution **TELEVISION**. To solve puzzle, write down MATE (an officer of a merchant vessel who ranks next below captain or master). *Add* LEOPARD, making MATELEOPARD. *Subtract* OAR, leaving MTELEPAD. *Subtract* MA (nickname for MOTHER in 2 letters), leaving TELEPD. *Add* VISOR, making TELEPDVISOR. *Add* UY, making TELEPDVISORUY. *Subtract* PD (abbreviation for Police Department), leaving TELEVISORUY. *Subtract* YOUR (the possessive form of YOU), leaving TELEVIS. *Add* ION, making **TELEVISION**.

(from page 92)
Correct solution **BACH**. To solve puzzle, write down BOA. *Add* STOLE, making BOASTOLE. *Subtract* STOOL, leaving BAE. *Add* CHEST, making BAECHEST. *Add* N, making BAECHESTN. *Subtract* NEST, leaving BACHE. *Subtract* E, leaving **BACH**.

(from page 93)
Correct solution **SPARKMAN**. To solve puzzle, write down BOWSPRIT. *Add* LEG, making BOWSPRITLEG. *Subtract* TOWEL, leaving BSPRIG. *Subtract* RIB, leaving SPG. *Add* ARK, making SPGARK. *Add* MAN (opposite of woman), making SPGARKMAN. *Subtract* G, leaving **SPARKMAN**.

(from page 94)
Correct solution **TAMPA**. To solve puzzle, write down CLEOPATRA (last Queen of Egypt and famous siren). *Add* N, making CLEOPATRAN. *Subtract* NERO (Roman emperor who fiddled while Rome burned), leaving CLPATA. *Subtract* CLP, leaving ATA. *Add* MP (abbreviation for Mounted Police), making ATAMP. *Subtract* A, leaving TAMP. *Add* A, making **TAMPA**.

(from page 95)
Correct solution **UNIVERSITY**. To solve puzzle, write down UNICORN. *Subtract* CORN, leaving UIN. *Add* L, making UINL. *Add* DIVER, making UINLDIVER. *Subtract* LID, leaving UNIVER. *Add* S, making UNIVERS. *Add* CITY (4-letter noun for big town), making UNIVERSCITY. *Subtract* C, leaving **UNIVERSITY**.

(from page 96)
Correct solution **ACHES**. To solve puzzle, write down HUARACHES. *Add* NUT, making HUARACHESNUT. *Add* GG, making HUARACHESNUTGG. *Subtract* RUG, leaving HAACHESNUTG. *Subtract* HUG (3-letter verb meaning to EMBRACE TIGHTLY WITH THE ARMS), leaving AACHESNT. *Subtract* NAT, leaving **ACHES**.

(from page 97)
Correct solution **OKINAWA**. To solve puzzle, write down MOCK (verb meaning to scoff or jeer). *Add* TINE, making MOCKTINE. *Add* A, making MOCKTINEA. *Add* WALRUS, making MOCKTINEAWALRUS. *Add* DD, making MOCKTINEAWALRUSDD. *Subtract* CURDLED (adjective meaning CLABBERED OR COAGULATED), leaving MOKTINAWAS. *Subtract* T, leaving MOKINAWAS. *Subtract* MS (abbreviation for MANUSCRIPT), leaving **OKINAWA**.

(from page 98)
Correct solution **COMMODORE**. To solve puzzle, write down HIGHBOY. *Add* COMMODE, making HIGHBOYCOMMODE. *Add* RR (abbreviation

174

for RAILROAD), making HIGHBOY-COMMODERR. *Subtract* DRIER, leaving HGHBOYCOMMO. *Add* A, making HGHBOYCOMMOA. *Add* DHOW, making HGHBOYCOMMOA-DHOW. *Subtract* GB (abbreviation for Great Britain), leaving HHOY-COMMOADHOW. *Subtract* HWH, leaving OYCOMMOADHO. *Subtract* AHOY (a nautical call in 4 letters used in hailing), leaving COMMODO. *Add* R, making COMMODOR. *Add* REF-EREE (7-letter word for a judge of play in certain games and sports), making COMMODORREFEREE. *Subtract* REEFER (slang for a cigarette containing marijuana), leaving **COM-MODORE.**

(from page 99)
Correct solution **STEVENSON.** To solve puzzle, write down US (abbreviation for United States). *Add* BALUS-TRADE, making USBALUSTRADE. *Add* KV, making USBALUSTRADE-KV. *Subtract* AUK, leaving SBLUS-TRADEV. *Add* BEACON, making SBLUSTRADEVBEACON. *Add* SK, making SBLUSTRADEVBEA-CONSK. *Add* ACORN, making SBLU-STRADEVBEACONSKACORN. *Subtract* ROD, leaving SBLUSTAEV-BEACNSKACORN. *Subtract* ABA-CUS, leaving LSTEVBENSKACORN. *Subtract* RACK, leaving LSTEVBEN-SON. *Subtract* BL (abbreviation for bill of lading), leaving **STEVENSON.**

(from page 100)
Correct solution **MOLASSES.** To solve puzzle, write down MOON. *Add* MOS, making MOONMOS. *Add* LORG-NETTE, making MOONMOSLORG-NETTE. *Add* EYEGLASSES, making MOONMOSLORGNETTEEYE-GLASSES. *Add* C, making MOONMOS-LORGNETTEEYEGLASSESC. *Subtract* MONOCLE, leaving MOSORG-NTTEEYEGLASSES. *Subtract* EYE, leaving MOSORGNTTEGLASSES. *Subtract* EGGS, leaving MOORNT-TLASSES. *Subtract* TON (2,000 lbs.), leaving MORTLASSES. *Subtract* TR, leaving **MOLASSES.**

(from page 101)
Correct solution **HARD.** To solve puzzle, write down NAPOLEON (French General and Emperor who met his defeat at Waterloo). *Add* HARVARD, making NAPOLEONHARVARD. *Add* MGL, making NAPOLEONHAR-VARDMGL. *Subtract* MAGELLAN (last name of a Portuguese navigator who discovered Philippine Islands), leaving NPOOHRVARD. *Subtract* PO (abbreviation for Post Office), leaving NOHRVARD. *Subtract* NO (opposite of YES), leaving HRVARD. *Subtract* RV, leaving **HARD.**

(from page 102)
Correct solution **GERMANY.** To solve puzzle, write down GERANIUM. *Add* HANDS, making GERANIUM-HANDS. *Add* CUFF, making GER-ANIUMHANDSCUFF. *Subtract* HANDCUFFS, leaving GERIMANU. *Add* YO, making GERIMANUYO. *Subtract* IOU (business term in 3 letters for a written acknowledgement of a debt), leaving **GERMANY.**

(from page 103)
Correct solution **BARTER.** To solve puzzle, write down BARTENDER. *Add* F, making BARTENDERF. *Subtract* FENDER, leaving BATR. *Subtract* T, leaving BAR. *Add* TIE, making BARTIE. *Subtract* I (9th letter of English alphabet), leaving BARTE. *Add* R, making **BARTER.**

(from page 104)
Correct solution **QUARTZ.** To solve puzzle, write down AQUARIUM. *Add* A, making **AQUARIUMA.** *Add* ROD, making **AQUARIUMAROD.** *Subtract* DRUM, leaving **AQUAIARO.** *Add* DS, making **AQUAIARODS.** *Subtract* SAID (past participle of verb SAY),

leaving AQUARO. *Add* TZ, making AQUAROTZ. *Subtract* OA, leaving **QUARTZ.**

(from page 105)
Correct solution **SIMPLE.** To solve puzzle, write down SIPHON. *Add* EAE, making SIPHONEAE. *Subtract* HONE, leaving SIPAE. *Add* S, making SIPAES. *Add* WIMPLE, making SIPAESWIMPLE. *Subtract* SAW, leaving IPESIMPLE. *Subtract* PIE, leaving **SIMPLE.**

(from page 106)
Correct solution **URAL.** To solve puzzle, write down HUNTER. *Add* YARD (distance of 3 FEET), making HUNTERYARD. *Subtract* E, leaving HUNTRYARD. *Subtract* HYDRANT, leaving UR. *Add* AL, making **URAL.**

(from page 107)
Correct solution **TEPID.** To solve puzzle, write down EINSTEIN (last name of physicist who developed theory of relativity). *Add* LO, making EINSTEINLO. *Subtract* NELSON (last name of English admiral and naval hero who fell in love with Lady Hamilton), leaving ITEI. *Subtract* II, leaving TE. *Add* PID, making **TEPID.**

(from page 108)
Correct solution **QUISLING.** To solve puzzle, write down QUILT. *Add* K, making QUILTK. *Subtract* KILT, leaving QU. *Add* IS, (singular form of ARE), making QUIS. *Add* SLING, making QUISSLING. *Subtract* S, leaving **QUISLING.**

(from page 109)
Correct solution **CURIE.** To solve puzzle, write down CARIBOU. *Add* K, making CARIBOUK. *Subtract* BARK, leaving CIOU. *Add* ARGALI, making CIOUARGALI. *Add* EDL, making CIOUARGALIEDL. *Subtract* LOG, leaving CIUARAIEDL. *Subtract*

DIAL, leaving CURAIE. *Subtract* A (first letter of English alphabet), leaving **CURIE.**

(from page 110)
Correct solution **HOPALONG.** To solve puzzle, write down HORSE. *Add* A, making HORSEA. *Add* PAL (slang for a good friend), making HORSEAPAL. *Add* NEST, making HORSEAPALNEST. *Add* U, making HORSEAPALNESTU. *Subtract* NURSE, leaving HOAPALEST. *Subtract* EAST (opposite of West), leaving HOPAL. *Add* TONGS, making HOPALTONGS. *Subtract* ST (abbreviation for Saint), leaving **HOPALONG.**

(from page 111)
Correct solution **LEMBERG.** To solve puzzle, write down CASTLE. *Add* MM, making CASTLEMM. *Subtract* MAST, leaving CLEM. *Add* BEAR, making CLEMBEAR. *Add* TAG, making CLEMBEARTAG. *Subtract* CAT, leaving LEMBERAG. *Subtract* A, leaving **LEMBERG.**

(from page 112)
Correct solution **ROAST BEEF.** To solve puzzle, write down ROWBOAT. *Subtract* BOW, leaving ROAT. *Subtract* T, leaving ROA. *Add* ST (abbreviation for SAINT), making ROAST. *Add* BEE, making ROASTBEE. *Add* F, making **ROAST BEEF.**

(from page 113)
Correct solution **COSTELLO.** To solve puzzle, write down COLUMBUS (last name of man who discovered America in 1492). *Add* LR, making COLUMBUSLR. *Subtract* BULL, leaving COMUSR. *Subtract* RUM (alcoholic liquor distilled from molasses and popular in Cuba), leaving COS. *Add* MAT, making COSMAT. *Subtract* AM (abbreviation for ante meridiem), leaving COST. *Add* HELLO (exclamation to express greeting used over tele-

phone), making COSTHELLO. *Subtract* H, leaving **COSTELLO.**

(from page 114)
Correct solution **UN.** To solve puzzle, write down LAUNDRY. *Subtract* DRY (opposite of WET), leaving LAUN. *Add* MP (abbreviation for MOUNTED POLICE), making LAUNMP. *Subtract* LAMP, leaving **UN.**

(from page 115)
Correct solution **ISOTOPES.** To solve puzzle, write down SCISSORS. *Add* KO (abbreviation for KNOCKOUT), making SCISSORSKO. *Add* EO, making SCISSORSKOEO. *Subtract* SOCKS, leaving ISRSOEO. *Add* TOP, making ISRSOEOTOP. *Add* ES, making ISRSOEOTOPES. *Subtract* ROSE, leaving **ISOTOPES.**

(from page 116)
Correct solution **DOGE.** To solve puzzle, write down SPEEDOMETER. *Subtract* TREE, leaving SPDOMEE. *Add* TAG, making SPDOMEETAG. *Subtract* PEAS, leaving DOMETG. *Subtract* EMT, leaving DOG. *Add* E, making **DOGE.**

(from page 117)
Correct solution **ANKARA.** To solve puzzle, write down SWEATER. *Add* TANK, making SWEATERTANK. *Subtract* SWATTER, leaving EANK. *Add* DAR (abbreviation for DAUGHTERS OF AMERICAN REVOLUTION), making EANKDAR. *Add* A, making EANKDARA. *Subtract* ED (2-letter short form for Edward), leaving **ANKARA.**

(from page 118)
Correct solution **KOREA.** To solve puzzle, write down KIMONO. *Add* TO, making KIMONOTO. *Add* MOP, making KIMONOTOMOP. *Add* UNREAL, (adjective in 6 letters meaning imaginary or fictitious), making KIMONO-TOMOPUNREAL. *Subtract* UN (ab-breviation for United Nations), leaving KIMOOTOMOPNREAL. *Subtract* MOON, leaving KITOMOPREAL. *Subtract* TOP, leaving KIMOREAL. *Subtract* LI (abbreviation for Long Island), leaving KMOREA. *Subtract* M, leaving **KOREA.**

(from page 119)
Correct solution **COB.** To solve puzzle, write down NEWSBOY. *Add* STAND, making NEWSBOYSTAND. *Subtract* NEWSSTAND, leaving BOY. *Add* O, making BOYO. *Add* COMB, making BOYOCOMB. *Subtract* MOB (noun in 3 letters which is a synonym for crowd), leaving YOCOB. *Subtract* YO, leaving **COB.**

(from page 120)
Correct solution **CAIN.** To solve puzzle, write down COMPASS. *Add* RI (abbreviation for RHODE ISLAND), making COMPASSRI. *Add* TRAIN, making COMPASSRITRAIN. *Subtract* PARROT, leaving CMSSIAIN. *Subtract* MISS (4-letter term of address to an unmarried woman), leaving **CAIN.**

(from page 121)
Correct solution **ALBERTA.** To solve puzzle, write down APPLE. *Add* I, making APPLEI. *Subtract* PIPE, leaving AL. *Add* H, making ALH. *Add* RUBBERS, making ALHRUBBERS. *Subtract* BRUSH, leaving ALBER. *Add* TA, making **ALBERTA.**

(from page 122)
Correct solution **ELEPHANT.** To solve puzzle, write down CAMEL. *Add* TURTLE, making CAMELTURTLE. *Add* WSP, making CAMELTURTLE-WSP. *Subtract* WALRUS, leaving CMETTLEP. *Subtract* MC, leaving ETTLEP. *Add* HAND, making ET-TLEPHAND. *Add* T, making ETTLE-PHANDT. *Subtract* DTT, leaving **ELEPHANT.**

(from page 123)

Correct solution **PARK**. To solve puzzle, write down CLAMP. *Add* PINEAPPLE, making CLAMPPINEAPPLE. *Subtract* LAMP, leaving CPINEAPPLE. *Subtract* APPLE, leaving CINPE. *Subtract* PINE (to languish or grieve), leaving C. *Add* PARROT, making CPARROT. *Add* KSK, making CPARROTKSK. *Subtract* STORK, leaving CPARK. *Subtract* C, leaving **PARK**.

(from page 124)

Correct solution **SHANGHAI**. To solve puzzle, write down SHOE. *Add* A, making SHOEA. *Add* RABBIT, making SHOEARABBIT. *Add* NGH, making SHOEARABBITNGH. *Add* PAIL, making SHOEARABBITNGHPAIL. *Subtract* RIB, leaving SHOEAABTNGHPAIL. *Subtract* TABLE, leaving SHOANGHPAI. *Subtract* OP, leaving **SHANGHAI**.

(from page 125)

Correct solution **ADONIS**. To solve puzzle, write down CANOE. *Subtract* CONE, leaving A. *Add* CANDLE, making ACANDLE. *Subtract* CE, leaving AANDL. *Add* TELEPHONE, making AANDLTELEPHONE. *Add* IS, making AANDLTELEPHONEIS. *Subtract* ELEPHANT, leaving ADLONEIS. *Subtract* EL, leaving **ADONIS**.

(from page 126)

Correct solution **DIAMOND**. To solve puzzle, write down DENTIST. *Add* LAMP, making DENTISTLAMP. *Subtract* PET (3-letter word for A TAMED HOUSE ANIMAL), leaving DNISTLAM. *Add* CONE, making DNISTLAMCONE. *Add* DU, making DNISTLAMCONEDU. *Subtract* NUTS (A SQUIRREL'S FAVORITE FOOD in 4 letters), leaving DILAMCONED. *Subtract* LEC, leaving **DIAMOND**.

(from page 127)

Correct solution **GLAND**. To solve puzzle, write down EAGLE. *Add* HAND, making EAGLEHAND. *Subtract* EH, making AGLEAND. *Add* TOM (nickname for THOMAS in 3 letters), making AGLEANDTOM. *Subtract* MA (affectionate term for your MOTHER in 2 letters), leaving GLEANDTO. *Subtract* TOE, leaving **GLAND**.

(from page 128)

Correct solution **FOSTER**. To solve puzzle, write down FROG. *Add* BASKET, making FROGBASKET. *Add* C, making FROGBASKETC. *Subtract* CAKE, leaving FROGBST. *Subtract* RG, leaving FOBST. *Add* EAR, making FOBSTEAR. *Subtract* BA, leaving **FOSTER**.

(from page 129)

Correct solution **EDISON**. To solve puzzle, write down BULB. *Subtract* LB, leaving UB. *Add* RECORD, making UBRECORD. *Add* NSI, making UBRECORDNSI. *Subtract* BUS, leaving RECORDNI. *Subtract* CORN, leaving ERDI. *Add* SPOON, making ERDISPOON. *Subtract* PRO, leaving **EDISON**.

(from page 130)

Correct solution **VANILLA**. To solve puzzle, write down VANE. *Add* LID, making VANELID. *Add* BULLDOG, making VANELIDBULLDOG. *Subtract* BUD (a flower not wholly expanded), leaving VANELILLDOG. *Add* A, making VANELILLDOGA. *Subtract* DOGE (the chief magistrate of the old republics of Venice and Genoa), leaving VANLILLA. *Subtract* L, leaving VANILLA. *Add* CRESSET, making VANILLACRESSET. *Subtract* SE (abbreviation for Southeast), leaving VANILLACRSET. *Subtract* CREST (5-letter word for figure above the escutcheon in a coat of arms), leaving **VANILLA**.

Answers to
Famous People Quiz

(from pages 150 to 161)

1—ARISTOTLE

2—PERICLES

3—CLEOPATRA

4—JULIUS CAESAR

5—MICHELANGELO

6—DA VINCI

7—NEWTON

8—REMBRANDT

9—RAPHAEL

10—JOHANN SEBASTIAN BACH

11—BEETHOVEN

12—MOZART

13—RICHARD WAGNER

14—ELIZABETH I

15—SHAKESPEARE

16—GOETHE

17—NAPOLEON

18—LISTER

19—HAWTHORNE

20—CHOPIN

21—PASTEUR

22—BENJAMIN FRANKLIN

23—CEZANNE

24—VAN GOGH

25—THOMAS JEFFERSON

26—GEORGE WASHINGTON

27—DARWIN

28—MARIE CURIE

29—DICKENS

30—TOLSTOY

31—GANDHI

32—WRIGHT BROTHERS

33—SARAH BERNHARDT

34—THOMAS EDISON

35—MARK TWAIN

Answers to Quiz
on Page 135

Alice's Adventures in Wonderland	Carroll
Paradise Lost	Milton
Huckleberry Finn	Mark Twain
The Scarlet Letter	Hawthorne
Droll Tales	Balzac
Black Beauty	Sewell
Origin of the Species	Darwin
The Divine Comedy	Dante
Tale of Two Cities	Dickens
Hamlet	Shakespeare
The Rise and Fall of the Roman Empire	Gibbon
The Odyssey	Homer
Gulliver's Travels	Swift
Little Women	Alcott
Moby Dick	Melville
Tom Jones	Fielding
Aeneid	Vergil
Pride and Prejudice	Austen
The Call of the Wild	Conrad
War and Peace	Tolstoy
The Decameron	Boccaccio

Answers to the World's Great Inventions

(from pages 137 to 139)

INVENTION	INVENTOR
Airplane (motor driven)	WRIGHT BROS.
Automobile Engine (2-stroke)	BENZ
Bakelite	BAEKELAND
Barometer	TORRICELLI
Cash Register	RITTY
Cellophane	BRANDENBERGER
Cotton Gin	WHITNEY
Diesel Engine	DIESEL
Dynamite	NOBEL
Elevator (brake)	OTIS
Ether (as anaesthetic)	LONG
Food Preservation (by sterilization, etc.)	APPERT
Fountain Pen	WATERMAN
Gas Burner	BUNSEN
Harvester	MOORE
Incandescent Lamp	EDISON
Lawn Mower	HILLS
Lightning Rod	FRANKLIN
Linoleum	WALTON

(continued from page 181)

Linotype	MERGENTHALER
Machine Gun	GATLING
Microphone	BERLINER
Motion Picture Machine	EDISON
Oleomargarine	MEGE-MOURIES
Pendulum	GALILEO
Piano	CRISTOFORI
Pistol (revolver)	COLT
Printing Press (rotary)	HOE
Reaper	Mc CORMICK
Rubber (vulcanized)	GOODYEAR
Safety Pin	HUNT
Sewing Machine	HOWE
Silencer	MAXIM
Stethoscope	LAENNEC
Telegraph (magnetic)	MORSE
Telegraph (wireless - high frequency)	MARCONI
Telephone	BELL
Television	BAIRD
Thermometer (mercurial)	FAHRENHEIT
Tire (pneumatic)	THOMPSON
Torpedo (self-propelled)	WHITEHEAD
Tractor (caterpillar)	HOLT
Typewriter	MITTERHOFFER
X-Ray	ROENTGEN

Correct Solutions to Wise Men's Sayings

(from pages 144 to 149)

Correct solution | AS | YOU | MAKE | YOUR | BED | SO | MUST | YOU | LIE | IN | IT |

To solve puzzle, write down HASH (poor man's dish of ground-up and cooked left-over meat). *Subtract* HH, leaving AS. Put AS in first 2 squares. Next write YOU (the letter U) in the following diagram of 3 squares. Now write down MAKE (M+RAKE—R) and insert it in next diagram. Next write YOUR (Y+HOUR[period of 60 minutes]—H) in the following diagram of 4 squares. Now write BED in the next 3 squares. Then write SO in the next diagram. Now write down MUST (MUG+ST—G) and insert it in the following diagram. Write YOU (U) in the next diagram. Next, write LIE (*an untruth*) in the next blank squares. Now put IN (WIN—W) in the following diagram. Then put IT (HIT—H) in the last diagram.

Correct solution | A | BIRD | IN | THE | HAND | IS | WORTH | TWO | IN | THE | BUSH |

To solve puzzle, put A in the first box. Next insert BIRD in the following 4 blank squares. Now write IN (opposite of OUT) in the next diagram. Then write THE (PITCHER—RIP[to tear]—C) in the following diagram. Now put HAND in the next squares. Now comes IS (singular of ARE) for the following diagram. Next write WORTH (5-letter noun meaning *The value of something*) in the following diagram. Now comes TWO (2) for the next 3 squares. Next write down IN THE (WINTER—WER+HEAD—AD) in the following two diagrams. Finally, write down BUSH in the last diagram.

Correct solution | HANDSOME | IS | AS | HANDSOME | DOES |

To solve puzzle, write down HANDSOME (HANDS+ROME—R) in the first diagram. Next put IS (FISH—FH) in the next diagram. Now write down AS (MAST—MT) in the following blank squares. Now comes HANDSOME (HAM+ND—M+SOME [*first word in Sophie Tucker's most popular song*]) for the next diagram. Finally, write DOES in the last diagram.

Correct solution | THE | EARLY | BIRD | CATCHES | THE | WORM |

To solve puzzle, write THE (T+HEN—N) in the first diagram. Next write EARLY (opposite of LATE) in the following diagram. Now comes BIRD in the third diagram. Then write CATCHES (CATCHER+S—R) in the next blank squares. Now put THE (THIMBLE—LIMB) in the following diagram. Finally, write WORM in the last diagram.

(continued from page 183)

Correct solution M A R R Y   I N   H A S T E   A N D   R E P E N T   A T   L E I S U R E

To solve puzzle, write down MARRY in the first diagram. Next put IN (DIN—D) in the following blank squares. Now comes HASTE (HAY+ST) for the next diagram. Then write AND (&) in the next diagram. Now put REPENT (RE+PEN+T) in the next squares. Then write AT (HAT—H) in the following 2 boxes. Finally, put LEISURE (NIPPLE—PIN+DISH+CURE—PDHC) in the last diagram.

Correct solution T H E   A P P L E   D O E S   N O T   F A L L   F A R   F R O M   T H E   T R E E

To solve puzzle, write THE (TH[*abbreviation for Territory of Hawaii*]+E) in the first 3 blank squares. Next put APPLE in the following diagram. Then write DOES (D+BUZZ—B) in the next diagram. Now put NOT (KNOT) in the following 3 blank boxes. Next put FALL in the next diagram. Now comes FAR (opposite of NEAR) in the following boxes. Next write FROM (FROG+M—G) in the following diagram. Then put THE in the next diagram. Finally, write TREE in the last diagram.

❦

Solution to Puzzle on pages (A) and (B).

Write down FORE. *Add* WORD (SWORD—S), making FOREWORD.

Now write BEE. *Add* FOUR (4). *Add* YOU (U). *Add* GO (GOAT—AT). *Add* TWO.

So far you now have BEFORE YOU GO TOO.

On the next line, start with FAR (opposite of NEAR). *Add* IN THIS (PIN—P+TH+DAISY—DAY). *Add* BOOK. This gives you IN THIS BOOK.

Now write GET (MAGNET—MAN [an adult male]). *Add* YOURSELF (Y+HOUR+SHELF—HH), making GET YOURSELF.

Next, write A. Now *add* COMFORTABLE (COMB+FORK—KB+TABLE). Now *add* CHAIR, making A COMFORTABLE CHAIR.

Now write NEXT (N+EXTRA—RA).

Then write SHARPEN (SHARP+PEN—P). Next write YOUR (possessive form of YOU). *Add* PENCILS, making SHARPEN YOUR PENCILS.

Next write AND (&). *Add* YOUR WITS (Y+FOUR+WITCHES—CHEF).

Next comes NOW (opposite of THEN). *Add* ENJOY (E+BANJO+Y—BA). *Add* YOURSELF (Y+SOUR [opposite of SWEET] +SEAL+F—SA), making NOW ENJOY YOURSELF.

Then write AND LET'S (HAND+RIFLE—HRIF+TS). *Add* SEE (C), making AND LET'S SEE.

Finally, write HOW (H+OWL—L). *Add* CLEVER (CLIP+EE—PIE+VEST—ST+R). *Add* YOU ARE (U R).

Now you finally have it: BEFORE YOU GO TOO FAR IN THIS BOOK, GET YOURSELF A COMFORTABLE CHAIR. NEXT SHARPEN YOUR PENCILS AND YOUR WITS. NOW ENJOY YOURSELF AND LET'S SEE HOW CLEVER YOU ARE.

184